WHEELCHAIR
TO
INDEPENDENCE

WHEELCHAIR

TO

INDEPENDENCE

Architectural Barriers Eliminated

By

ERNEST M. GUTMAN
Fort Lauderdale, Florida

With

CAROLYN R. GUTMAN

With a Foreword by

Howard A. Rusk, M.D.
Director, Institute of Rehabilitation Medicine
New York University Medical Center
New York, New York

CHARLES C THOMAS · PUBLISHER
Springfield · Illinois · U.S.A.

Published and Distributed Throughout the World by
CHARLES C THOMAS · PUBLISHER
BANNERSTONE HOUSE
301-327 East Lawrence Avenue, Springfield, Illinois, U.S.A.
NATCHEZ PLANTATION HOUSE
735 North Atlantic Boulevard, Fort Lauderdale, Florida, U.S.A.

With THOMAS BOOKS *careful attention is given to all details of
manufacturing and design. It is the Publisher's desire to present books
that are satisfactory as to their physical qualities and artistic possibilities
and appropriate for their particular use.* THOMAS BOOKS *will be true
to those laws of quality that assure a good name and good will.*

Printed in the United States of America
H-13

Dedicated
to
Planners with
Heart and Brain

FOREWORD

THE RELATIONSHIP between architectural barriers and educational and employment problems came into more meaningful perspective as the result of the research and demonstration grants program of the Rehabilitation Service Administration (then the Vocational Rehabilitation Administration).

Among such projects were studies on the housing needs of the handicapped, special clothing needs, and modification of structures, tools, machinery, and office and household equipment.

In 1958 at a White House meeting of the Advisory Council to the President's Committee on Employment of the Handicapped, an *ad hoc* group consisting of Mr. Sumner Whittier then Administrator of Veterans Affairs, Miss Mary E. Switzer then Director of the Office of Rehabilitation, and Mr. Robert Goodwin of the Department of Labor was created.

The story of what has transpired in the succeeding ten years regarding the foregoing is clearly told in this book of Mr. Gutman.

The last chapter on the subject, however, has not been written, nor will it be written until all the architectural barriers which limit the mobility of persons with physical disabilities have been removed.

Mr. Gutman's book will contribute significantly to this end-objective by establishing greater understanding among more people who are closely involved with the problem of eliminating architectural barriers.

Probably the greatest goal of a disabled person with impaired ambulation, is mobility. This is true from the functional sense as well as psychologically, as mobility is a symbol of independence. I have seen this goal attained daily at the Institute of Rehabilitation Medicine, New York University Medical Center, during the past twenty years.

The greatest motivation of disabled patients to continue the long and arduous task of rehabilitation is that increased mobility will result from their hard work.

Unfortunately, despite the increased mobility our disabled fellow citizens may have achieved through their own efforts and the techniques of modern rehabilitation, many doors are closed to them because of architectural barriers. They often do not find conditions in public buildings that permit the freedom of motion, such as exist in rehabilitation surroundings.

Happily, within the last decade there has been a growing public awareness of the problem, and a recognition that something can be done to remedy the evil.

The effort to correct poor structural conditions for the benefit of the disabled had its inception with the late Hugo Deffner of Oklahoma City. A handicapped person himself, Mr. Deffner was a persistent, articulate "voice in the wilderness" when few others recognized the existence of architectural barriers as a problem that should be done away with.

This book by Mr. Gutman, aptly entitled *Wheelchair to Independence,* demonstrates by words and numerous illustrations many methods of how it can be accomplished.

HOWARD A. RUSK, M.D.

PREFACE

ALMOST TWO HUNDRED years ago, our forefathers coined a treasured document whose immortal language included the meaningful words, "life, liberty, and the pursuit of happiness." Subsequently, there occurred "the shot heard 'round the world." Politically speaking, the events that followed were eternally etched in the annals of history. The tyrant's grip was demolished!

Since man was created, another villain has existed who defies all challenges to his tyranny. That cruel jailor is "Physical Handicap."

In recent years, great progress has been made by science in the treatment of many afflictions With the united effort of physicians, physical therapists, rehabilitation centers, creators of ingenious prosthetic devices, and society in general, in many instances, the disabled are freed of the inhibiting shackles of "handicap."

However, despite the many improvements in their lot, the handicapped often are confronted with a heartbreaking bugaboo—insurmountable architectural barriers. How futile it is for a wheelchair-user, who learned to function independently in rehabilitation surroundings, to find himself in an outside world loaded with structural stumbling blocks. What a blow it is for a well-qualified applicant to be rejected for a good job merely because doorways to the office building or to the washrooms therein were too narrow for his wheelchair! Perhaps stairs impede his entry!

It is a recognized fact that in industry, the disabled equals, and often exceeds, his nondisabled brethren in productivity. As a result, industrial portals are being opened wider every day to this ever-growing segment of our population.

At present, almost 20 per cent of our citizens may be considered among the disabled, with two million more to be added in the next decade in the class of traumatic paraplegics alone. In addition, the startling prediction of leading authorities is that by 1980, for every able-bodied individual, there will be one person with a disability, chronic or otherwise.

The following are, in general, those groups with which society is mainly concerned:

1. The disabled aged in need of physical assistance.
2. Those with serious visual, hearing, and vocal defects.
3. Individuals with disabilities resulting primarily from lack of coordination or palsy.
4. The semiambulatory requiring crutches, canes, braces, or artificial legs because of amputation, along with the spastics, certain cardiacs, and arthritics whose walking is adversely affected.
5. The nonambulatory requiring the use of wheelchairs.

It is ironic that the large increase in the number of disabled may be attributed in part to the advancement of medical knowledge. Many who previously might have succumbed to their diseases are saved and may live for many years, even though they are disabled in some respect. Longevity is being continuously increased, resulting in many more aged with disabilities due to age.

The purpose of this book is to incorporate "under one roof" many suggestions and recommendations which will enable architects and builders to adapt and alter existing structures, both residential and public, for the benefit of the disabled, and to construct new buildings without architectural barriers.

No longer will the disabled feel as though they are in the confinement of a straight jacket in their own homes or places of business. Regardless of the structural impediment, it usually can be remedied. "There's more than one way to skin a cat!"

Ingress and egress to buildings will be easy because steps will be eliminated or replaced by ramps. No longer will it be necessary to seek out back doors, usually used for the receipt of supplies or through which garbage cans are slid. Passenger elevators will be large enough to accommodate a wheelchair. The blessings to the disabled may be a hundredfold if architectural barriers to their enjoying life are eliminated.

The benefits derived from improving conditions for the disabled may be likened to the ripples in a lake caused by a stone breaking its surface: the ripples spread in many directions. The disabled person is permitted to earn a living and thus provide for himself and family: he immediately becomes a taxpayer, his financial independence permits him to expend money on luxuries and entertainment, and so he contributes to the national economy. Not to be overlooked, whereas, in numerous instances, steps have acted as barriers to polling places, now the disabled will be permitted to exercise voting rights.

Although this book has as its principal target architectural obstructions that adversely affect wheelchair-users, everyone will benefit whether disabled or not. For instance, who wouldn't prefer to enter a building whose door is street level rather than being required to climb a flight of steps?

It will be a revolutionary step in the right direction if this writing becomes a shot heard throughout the world of builders, architects, and others interested in improved structural design, resulting in changing "life" to "living" for this ever-growing segment of the population.

With true independence acquired, the disabled person's pursuit of happiness will have become "happiness found."

GRATEFUL ACKNOWLEDGMENTS

To my wife, CAROLYN R. GUTMAN, for her sketches of residential floor plans, for an illustration of a bus with hydraulic lift for wheelchairs, and for her contribution of ideas as a home economist. She also made numerous worthwhile recommendations relating to the manuscript.

The following, alphabetically arranged, added much to the contents either directly or indirectly:

MRS. KATHLEEN C. ARNESON, *Executive Secretary, National Commission on Architectural Barriers, Department of Health, Education, and Welfare.*

ALBERT B. BAUER, R.A., *Director of Building Construction, City of New York, Department of Public Works.*

RALPH W. CAREY, *Director of Management, Housing Authority of the City of Miami, Florida.*

ROSS E. GUTMAN, D.D.S., M.P.H., *New York State Education Department.*

PHILIP M. HARTUNG, *Everest and Jennings, Inc., Los Angeles, California.*

JOHN E. KING, *President, Kansas State Teachers College, Emporia, Kansas.*

JOSEPH F. KONITZKI, *Assistant Director, Division of Rehabilitation-Education Services, University of Illinois, Champaign, Illinois.*

PAUL R. KRUM, *Secretary, Inclinator Company of America, Harrisburg, Pa.*

MRS. JOSEPH S. LAURIE (GINI), *Managing Editor of the TOOMEY-j-GAZETTE.*

ADRIAN LEVY, *Assistant Commissioner of Education for Vocational Rehabilitation, New York State, Department of Education.*

HENRY A. MALLON, *Assistant Administrative Director, Office of Special Education and Pupil Personnel Services, Board of Education of the City of New York.*

ROBERT P. MEIER, *Administrative Assistant, Eastern Paralyzed Veterans Association, New York City.*

EUGENE H. NICKERSON, *County Executive, Nassau County, Mineola, New York.*

DR. TIMOTHY NUGENT, *Director of the Rehabilitation Center, University of Illinois.*

MRS. BARBARA L. RASCON, *Secretary to the Director, Division of College Facilities, Department of Health, Education, and Welfare.*

H. I. ROMNES, *Chairman of the Board of Directors, American Telephone and Telegraph Company, New York City.*

WILLIAM R. SCALES, *Vocational Rehabilitation, Kansas State Teachers College, Emporia, Kansas.*

W. SCHIAVONI, *Engineering Director, Customer Telephone Systems, American Telephone and Telegraph Company, New York City.*

HARRY A. SCHWEIKERT, JR., *Executive Secretary, Eastern Paralyzed Veterans Association, New York City.*

Mrs. Nadine G. Simmons, *Public Information Supervisor, American Telephone and Telegraph Company, New York City.*

G. M. Smith, *Engineering Division, Customer Telephone Systems, American Telephone and Telegraph Company, New York City.*

Meyer F. Wiles, *Deputy and Acting Commissioner, City of New York, Department of Public Works.*

COOPERATING AGENCIES

Human Resources
Research and Training Institute
Albertson, New York

National Society for Crippled Children and Adults
2023 West Ogden Avenue
Chicago, Illinois

New York State University Construction Fund
194 Washington Avenue
Albany, New York

The Easter Seal Society
239 Park Avenue South
New York, New York

Institute of Rehabilitation Medicine
400 East 34th Street
New York, New York

Veterans Administration
Supervisory Appraiser
252 Seventh Avenue
New York, New York

E. M. G.

CONTENTS

ILLUSTRATIONS

WHEELCHAIR
TO
INDEPENDENCE

Chapter 1

HOME IS MORE THAN JUST A WHEELCHAIR

Do you have to worry every time you leave your residence, or return to it? Will there be someone to help you negotiate the steps? Are you going to be trapped in your own house, or barred from it?

At first blush, the endless list of structural villains seems overwhelmingly formidable, but, broken down with an astute and calculated attack, these barriers to your good life may be eliminated.

If you are an individual, sound in mind and spirit, why permit unsuitable living quarters to serve as a veritable prison? Because you must use a wheelchair instead of walking is a poor reason to permit yourself to become excluded from society. Physical immobilization compounded by a loss of social contact is a depressing prospect that may very well result in mental withdrawal from the mainstream of life, and then in hopeless surrender to your plight.

To retain the desire to fight back, you must have stimuli of mind and emotions. Otherwise, a satisfactory adjustment to your disability is not possible. Sometimes illnesses of mysterious origin are born simply because you've "thrown up your hands" in defeat. Is premature hospitalization to be your refuge? Ridiculous!

They say that it's the last push that can mean the difference between victory and defeat. This is especially valid in the case of a wheelchair-user. So, if architectural barriers are your nemeses, you are about to storm them with a frontal attack.

CONSIDERATIONS FOR THE INTERIOR

Let's say you're an apartment dweller. If, at the time that your affliction occurs you live on an upper floor of a walk-up building, the economic thing to do would be to try to get a street-level apartment in the same building.

Failing that, you may turn to the expedient of a hotel, usually too

[3]

expensive for Mr. Average. At least now your horizons need not be limited to the four walls! The contents of your purse will determine the amount of drive that you exert in searching for a suitable apartment.

The ideal residence is one right off the street and without any steps. Second best is an apartment in an elevator-equipped structure. Since mechanical lifts sometimes go out of order, the lowest possible floor is preferable, just in case an emergency may require you to be assisted from the premises without benefit of the elevator.

Finding the right place to live is so very important. Through rehabilitation training you may have learned many things about self-help, and you should be determined that all of this knowledge will not go down the drain, to be forgotten because of loss of incentive and lack of practice.

Newspaper advertisements may steer you in the right direction but will contain no information vital to meeting your requirements. Even a well-intentioned renting agent may not be able to give you a telephone answer as to what the stair situation is or how wide the doorways are. He may never have paid attention, for instance, to the two entry steps; but, to one in a wheelchair, a riser of only a few inches may be a dreadful obstruction.

The indisputable fact is that you or someone fully cognizant of your needs should physically examine the structure you are considering. Each individual has his own check list, but certain necessities are universal in nature for the wheelchair-user:

1. Are there impeding steps or risers?
2. Are doorways wide enough?
3. If there are hallways, are they accessible and adequate?
4. Are bathrooms large enough, with fixtures conveniently placed?
5. Is the kitchen convenient?
6. If an elevator is available, is it large enough?

Bathroom

Assuming the basic needs are suitable for your requirements, that is, the bathroom is large with fixtures well-placed, a most serious defect may exist—the door may be too narrow. Don't panic. All is not lost. There are two remedies:

1. If the landlord is cooperative, with his approval and usually at *your* expense, a competent workman can widen the doorway providing there is sufficient wall space for such an alteration. If the new opening is too wide for ordinary solid doors, an accordion type may suffice. Get at least two cost estimates (Fig. 1).

2. A more economical method of beating the skimpy-doorway problem is by using a simple crank-operated device that, when attached to a folding wheelchair, can narrow it several inches. It may be purchased complete at Rehabilitation Equipment, Inc., 175 East 83rd Street, New York, New York. Ask for NARRO-MATIC® (Fig. 2).

The bathroom may raise other problems, most of which can be surmounted:

What a frustration it is to have a toilet seat that is too low for you! To have the existing fixture raised would involve extensive alteration at a prohibitive cost. Well, don't give up the ship. A practical solution is to secure a commode which fits over the toilet and which may be adjusted to the desired height. Usually, the level of the wheelchair's seat is most convenient. Most surgical-appliance establishments carry a wide variety of commodes that will include a type which suits your needs and purse (Fig. 3).

How about bathing? The tub appears out of the question because of its sides? How will you get in and out?

Consult with your physical therapist as to the best line of action to take to make the tub safely accessible. The Hoyer® or a similar hydraulic lift may be attached to the side of the tub or may rest on its own base; by means of a boom, this can swing you, while seated in a sling attached to the contrivance, over the edge of the tub (Fig. 4). You may find it comfortable to have a bathtub seat to sit on rather than the tub's bottom. These seats come in a variety of models ranging from stools resting on rubber-tipped legs to seats that wedge between the sides of the tub (Fig. 5).

If you prefer the shower to tub bathing, you will be confronted by a slightly different question, that of how to utilize the fixed over-head shower so that a complete bathing job can be managed. That's an easy one to solve. Have the shower head changed to a long, flexible one. Secure a spray that attaches to the tub faucet by a long rubber tube. With the shower curtains drawn, you can spray to your heart's content.

Safety in the bathroom should be given prime consideration. Statistics show that it is here that a great many accidents at home occur because of slippery floors and standing in tubs. A precaution that may prevent or reduce the occurrence of such a calamity as a bad fall is the installation of strategically placed grab bars about the toilet and the bathtub area. These bars should be positioned as required by you (Fig. 6).

To add to your sense of security while entering or leaving the bathtub, adhesive strips are available on the market that may be attached to the edges for a firmer grip. These strips, when placed on the tub bottom, will give surer footing for one standing there. However, the friction will make it difficult for you to stretch out if you are seated on the tapes.

Safety bars that fit over the sides of most tubs may be purchased in many department stores as well as at surgical-appliance stores.

A suggested convenience to permit closer approach to the bathtub is a wheelchair with swiveling footrests which are removable. This will allow you to ride right up to the tub. You may find such approach to the toilet more convenient too.

Now let's see what can be done with the other rooms to add to your comfort. Alterations to the structure often are impossible or economically impractical. We must seek other remedies.

Bedroom

A fine bed that is too low for you may be raised to the desired height by placing appropriately cut blocks of wood under each leg.

If you have a large closet which can have bins built on the shelves for storage of items that normally would be placed in dressers, such items of furniture may be eliminated, thus adding to the floor space (Fig. 7).

The closet may be improved by installing a clothing bar at a suitable height. Shelves may be lowered, and hooks may be provided that can be easily reached.

Scatter rugs should be removed.

Kitchen

Obviously, fixtures cannot ordinarily be moved or changed except at great expense. However, certain rearrangements may prove helpful. If cabinet shelves may be lowered, have it done. They will be perfect for frequently used items. Magnetized hooks may be affixed to metal surfaces at desired heights.

Some handy gadgets affix to smooth surfaces by suction cups (towel racks and soap dishes, for example). A casual trip through a good hardware store may be a revelation to you concerning products that will enhance your home and ease of living.

Low cabinet doors should be utilized to the maximum. For instance, there are garbage receptacles that can be hung from the lower part of the door, thus eliminating the standard type which requires floor space. Many other articles in daily use will be most conveniently located when dangling from a door hook.

A dishwasher will make housekeeping more pleasant. There are reasonably priced portable ones which fit into surprisingly small spaces and which render excellent service. The only needed fittings are an electric wire that plugs into an ordinary house outlet and a flexible tubing that is affixed to the sink faucet.

If space permits, a combination washer-dryer for laundry will prove a boon. It occupies little more than 25 inches of floor space and costs less than the total price of washer and dryer if purchased separately.

An ironing board with adjustable height is a great convenience to one who must work from a wheelchair.

Dining Room

This area should not be cluttered with furniture. All that is needed is an extension table with four chairs belonging to a set. Additional chairs should be the folding type since they take less space at the table than do standard chairs, and they may be conveniently stored.

A lightweight table on easily rolling wheels will facilitate serving meals and clearing the dining table. The dining table should have no obstructions to prevent your knees from comfortably fitting beneath.

Attractive plastic and synthetic-fabric tablecloths are reasonably priced and require no laundry service: just a swish of a damp cloth for the plastic and a simple washing for the synthetic. These dry quickly and need no ironing. Easily cleaned place mats will make things even more facile.

Floors

Rugs make wheelchair propelling difficult because of the pile and should be avoided if possible. When carpeting is unavoidable, it should be the wall-to-wall type fastened down firmly.

Better floor coverings are sheet vinyl, asbestos tile, and vinyl tile. Floors should *not* be waxed.

TYPES OF RESIDENCES

Garden Apartment

Consisting of only a few stories, this apartment is usually located in the suburbs and is rarely equipped with elevators. A ground-floor apartment without entry steps in such a building would be excellent.

High-rise Apartment

These buildings have many stories and elevator service. There are three types:

1. *Cooperative.* An investor in this type of apartment actually purchases a proportional share in the entire building. Monthly charges cover the cost of the building's maintenance and upkeep; these charges are prorated among all shareholders of the co-op.

   The cost to each occupant will vary from time to time and will be subject to the services needed and the expense involved in performing them. Of course, increased charges in keeping the structure in good condition will probably result in higher monthly charges.

   It is strongly recommended that you have your attorney representing you when you are entering into a deal involving the purchase of a cooperative apartment.

2. *Condominium.* This type of purchase is quite different from buying a co-op. In this case, you actually end up owning a

specific apartment with legal title, as though you had bought a private home. You may do as you wish within the four walls of the apartment, as long as your acts do not infringe on the rights of other owners. Thus, you may make any alterations desired without first getting anyone's permission, as is actually required when a co-op is involved.

You may sell, rent, or mortgage the premises. Your monthly carrying charges are to reduce any outstanding balance due on the purchase price, plus interest, and a proportionate share of taxes and maintenance charges. The latter charges are used for hiring necessary help, general repair services, and taking care of landscaping. In many instances, the owners of condominium apartments have a social club on the premises with numerous amenities such as shuffleboard courts, swimming pool, and meeting room. Any cost for proper running of these features is equally divided among the members.

As in the purchase of a co-op, it is urged that you be represented by an attorney when you buy a condominium apartment.

In both the cooperative and condominium transactions, a great portion of the monthly payments may be income tax deductible. This phase should be discussed with your accountant or any other tax expert.

3. *Straight rental.* These apartments are rented on an annual or monthly basis or on such other basis as agreed upon by the parties. Although oral leases are sometimes entered into, the written contract is preferable and most binding.

   Leases are generally fairly standard and contain all items so as to state clearly the rights and obligations of both the landlord and tenant. Included in the lease are the following:
   a. The period covered and the exact commencing and termination dates.
   b. The precise address and apartment number.
   c. The amount of rent, and when paid (e.g., monthly).
   d. Whether the apartment may be sublet.
   e. Whether the lease may be canceled.
      (1) If so, under what conditions?
      (2) Does cancellation require monetary payment?

    f. Whether alteration may be made by tenant.
       (1) If so, at whose expense?
       (2) May tenant remove improvements at end of lease?
       (3) Must premises be restored to original condition when tenant vacates apartment?
    g. Detailed provisions for automobile parking space.
    h. Stipulations as to who pays for gas and electricity.
    i. Details if there is any rent concession.
    j. Provision for pets (if this applies to you).
    k. Whether doorman service is part of the deal.
       (1) If so, give details (whose expense, etc.).
    l. Whether tenant is required to deposit cash security with landlord.
       (1) If so, the amount thereof.
       (2) When is security to be returned to tenant?
       (3) Must landlord pay interest thereon (details)?
    m. Whether elevator service is to be provided by landlord.
       (1) Are elevators operator-controlled or self-service, and during what hours?
    n. Whether heat, hot water, janitorial service, and general maintenance and repairs are provided at landlord's expense.
       (1) Are painting and decorating done by landlord?

With the ever-increasing number of high-rise apartment houses, straight rental apartments have become more available with lower rents. The older apartments in most instances are more reasonable and, in some locales, are still rent controlled at levels that existed immediately after World War II.

However, all things being considered, it often is more desirable to settle in a new building if your finances can take it. Many of the new structures have central air-conditioning or have wiring adequate for air-conditioners, which are installed by the tenants themselves.

The new buildings offer better safety features such as fireproof facilities and better means for speedy, safe exit in case of emergency. This certainly is important to the wheelchair-confined dwellers.

For security against undesirable elements of society, the more exclusive buildings have doormen and elevator operators. These employees may be of physical assistance when called upon. It is a great comfort to know that there is always someone available in case you need help.

An innovation in more and more buildings is the closed-circuit television, with an operator constantly watching what is going on in remote parts of the structure. A self-service elevator, with such a watchdog, ceases to be a fearful cage. Also if there is anything that discourages a criminal from practicing his nefarious "profession," it is the fear of being seen.

If you discuss your needs with the landlord while the building is being constructed, for a reasonable consideration, alterations in the original plan may be made. Kitchen cabinets may be built lower, with conveniently spaced, adjustable, pull-out shelves. Appliances such as dishwashers may be built-in. Doors may be made wide enough to accommodate a wheelchair. Refrigerators may be ordered with doors swinging in the direction best for you. Jacks for telephone extensions may be installed at strategic locations. Electric light switches and outlets may be placed at convenient heights. Sills may be omitted at doorways between rooms. Clothes bars and shelves in closets may be placed at heights to suit you.

The beauty of having these items constructed to your specifications in the course of construction is that they will not add to the builder's costs in most cases and thus will cost you nothing. As a matter of fact, the things that you desire will make the apartment more desirable for the nondisabled who may rent it after you vacate the premises.

Municipal Housing

This housing in many communities, has started to adapt itself to a degree specifically for the benefit of the disabled, with various conveniences expressly for those in wheelchairs.

Such housing eliminates many environmental problems which those with infirmities need "like a hole in the head." These apartments are designed and built expressly for the disabled and are rented to them exclusively. Now these persons no longer need fear that suitable living quarters are not available for them or that they will be rejected as tenants because they are disabled. Of great importance, the economic barrier of installing special features has faded almost completely away. These can be quite costly and often are beyond the financial reach of the seriously disabled.

A case in point is the building program of the New York City Housing Authority. Many apartments are geared for occupancy by the aged, with farsighted provision in the event that these tenants become disabled. Ramps are provided to eliminate entry stairs. Kitchen cabinet shelves may be reached from a sedentary position (Fig. 8). Rooms are arranged without complicated twists for easy maneuvering of wheelchairs. Bathroom doors have catches that permit them to be opened inward or out. Thus, emergency access cannot be prevented if, for instance, the occupant falls against the door, blocking it from the inside. The bathroom floors are of non-skid material, and grab bars are appropriately placed in ample quantities. Some of these rooms have good-sized ride-in stall showers (Figs. 5, 6, and 9).

Private House

Let's turn to the private-house resident. After a number of years, the mortgage is paid off and the owner basks in the sunlight of his "enchanted cottage" that is free and clear of any monetary encumberance. Then "the fickle finger of Fate" points at him. From his wheelchair, the veil of perfection seems to be vaporizing. There are steps down to the lovely finished basement and up to the bedrooms. The obstacle of two steps leads to the entrance. Doorways seem to have shrunk and have become impassable. The list of deficiencies mounts in number daily. What should be done to keep the house's halo intact?

About the entry steps, a ramp that is not too steep will do the trick. As a safety factor it should have at least one handrail. Two are better (See Fig. 10).

As to the interior flights of stairs, a fairly economical elevator, enclosed in a shaft going to the upper floors from the basement, can be readily installed in most homes. For an elevator required between two floors only, no shaft is needed, resulting in less costly and much quicker installation. Cars of almost any size may be provided, as long as they are adequate to hold a wheelchair and as many passengers as may be expected to ride at one time. Gates that open in different directions on the various floors may be provided. Control buttons should be placed at convenient heights and positions. An emergency alarm signal is to be included in the elevator, with a telephone often provided as optional equipment.

For those able to switch from wheelchair to another seat and vice versa, an inclined elevator seat is supported by a steel channel secured to one side of the staircase, within which is the operating cable. This will carry the passenger to the desired floor. When not in use, the seat may be folded back so that the steps may be utilized. Obviously a wheelchair must be waiting for the rider at the desired floor. (This device, as well as the regular elevator, may be secured through Inclinator Company of America, 2200 Paxton Street, Harrisburg, Pennsylvania.)

Concerning the bedrooms, if made inaccessible because of stairs, see whether it is possible to convert a ground-floor room into sleeping quarters. This certainly is the quickest and most reasonable action to take.

Another device for defeating the nemesis of stairs is a lift suitable for straight staircases only, with obvious advantages. It consists of a platform 28 inches wide upon which a wheelchair with occupant may negotiate a flight of stairs. The platform is supported by a steel track fastened to a side of the stairway and is operated by an enclosed pull chain. Control buttons are conveniently placed. When not in use, the platform may be folded back, permitting normal use of the stairs (Fig. 11). (This appliance is available through Rehabilitation Equipment, Inc., 175 East 83rd Street, New York, New York.)

After weighing the pros and cons of your prospects of finding a suitable apartment to meet your physical requirements, or of altering your present residence, be it an apartment or private house, you will have reached a momentous decision. Alterations are not feasible because of cost and the physical characteristics of the premises? Forget the apartment! Buy a new house—or build a custom-made one!

FIGURE 1. Widened bathroom doorway with accordion door.

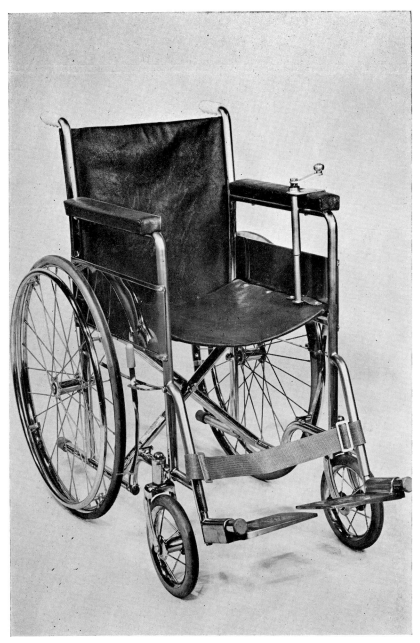

FIGURE 2. Wheelchair with a narrower attached. (Courtesy of Rehabilitation Equipment, Inc.)

FIGURE 3. Commode with adjustable legs.

FIGURE 4. Hoyer Lift, screened patio, rectangular pool.

FIGURE 5. Bathtub with seat and grab bars. (Courtesy of New York City Housing Authority.)

FIGURE 6. Bathtub grab bars. (Courtesy of New York City Housing Authority.)

FIGURE 7. Walk-in closet with bins.

FIGURE 8. Kitchen cabinets. (Courtesy of New York City Housing Authority.)

FIGURE 9. Stall shower, basin, ample floor space. (Courtesy of New York City Housing Authority.)

FIGURE 10. Two steps converted into one.

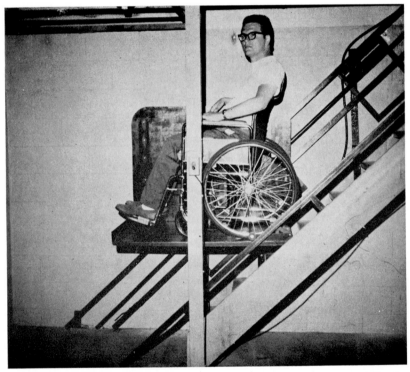

FIGURE 11. Wheelchair lift for straight staircase. (Courtesy of Rehabilitation Equipment, Inc.)

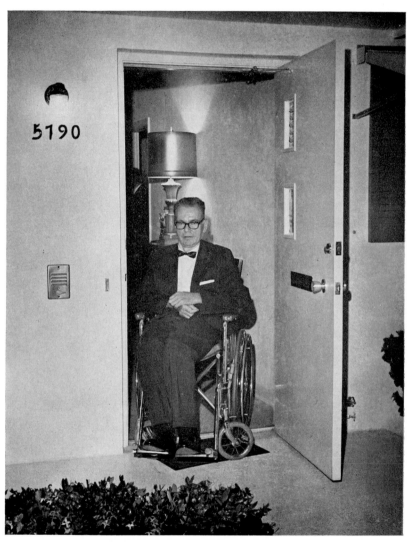

FIGURE 12. Ideal entrance.

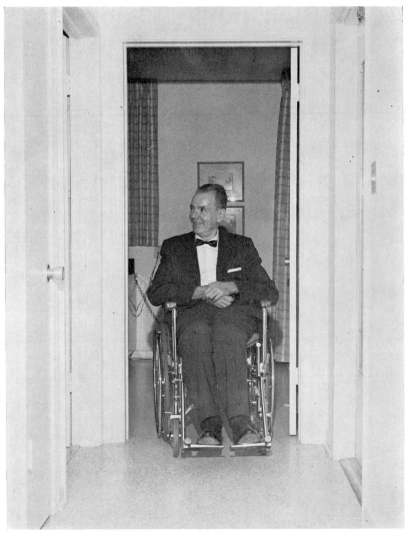

FIGURE 13. Wide doorways, spacious halls.

FIGURE 14. Kitchen with ample floor space. (Courtesy of New York City Housing Authority.)

FIGURE 15. Wall-hung commode with grab bars.

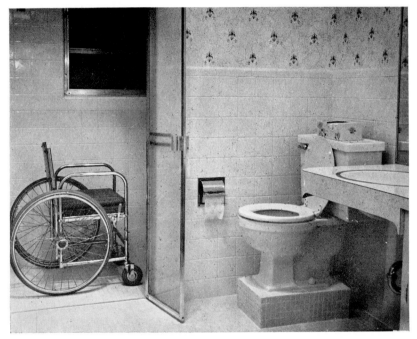

FIGURE 16. Bathroom with commode on pedestal, stall shower with shower wheelchair, basin with knee space.

FIGURE 17. Specially equipped shower in men's residence hall, Kansas State Teachers College. (Courtesy of the college.)

FIGURE 18. Specially equipped commode with grab bars, Kansas State Teachers College. (Courtesy of the college.)

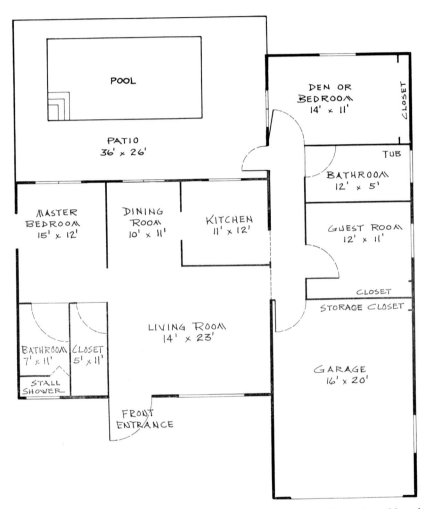

FIGURE 19. Three-bedroom residence, pool. Curved dotted lines show hinged doors; straight dotted lines show sliding doors (wood); doors to patio are sliding glass (shatterproof).

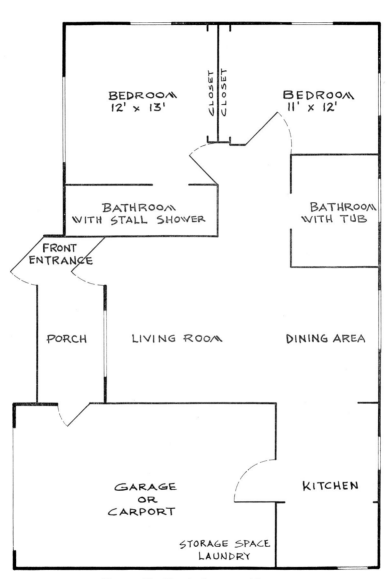

FIGURE 20. Two-bedroom residence.

FIGURE 21. Automatically operated doors by foot pressure.

FIGURE 22. Reserved parking space.

FIGURE 23. Type of ramp.

FIGURE 24. Ramp with adjoining reserved parking space.

FIGURE 25. Ramp entrance.

FIGURE 26. Street-level entrance.

FIGURE 27. Ramp entrance.

Figure 28. Example of beveled curbs, Kansas State Teachers College. (Courtesy of the college.)

FIGURE 29. Outside entrance to men's residence hall, Kansas State Teachers College. (Courtesy of the college.)

FIGURE 30. Ramp with metal hand rails at entrance to administration building, Kansas State Teachers College. (Courtesy of the college.)

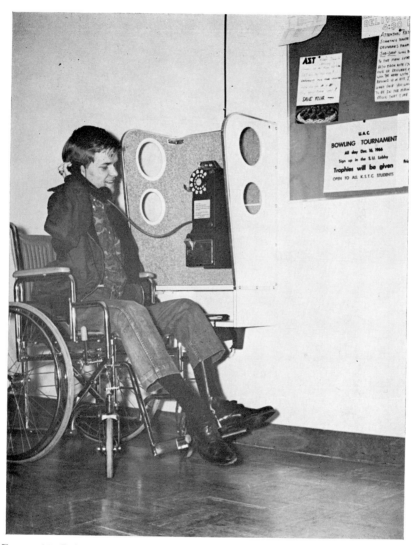

FIGURE 31. Public telephone that has been lowered for use of wheelchair students. Men's residence hall, Kansas State Teachers College. (Courtesy of the college.)

FIGURE 32. Dialing by push buttons. Ten buttons replace the customary dial on Bell Telephone System's new Touch-Tone® telephone. Tests with able-bodied users have shown that it is easier and more than twice as fast to tap out a call with the push buttons than to turn a conventional dial. Tests with severely handicapped individuals have shown that almost anyone, no matter how severe his disability, can operate the buttons.

Major modifications must be made in telephone company facilities in each location before the new service can be made available. Already available in many locations today, this convenience is expected to be available throughout the Bell System by the mid 1970's. (Courtesy of American Telephone and Telegraph.)

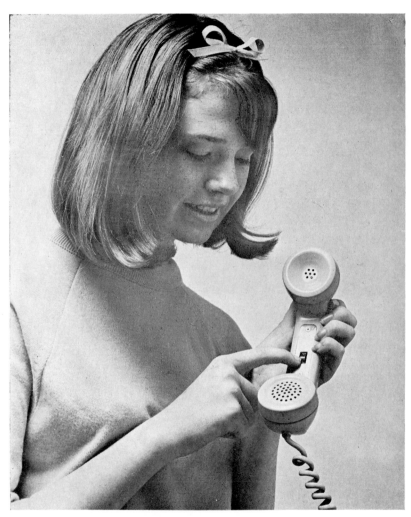

FIGURE 33. The volume control handset for the hard of hearing. The user can vary the amount of amplification by turning the little adjustment wheel on the underside of the handset handle. This handset may be used with the regular desk or wall phone, the Princess℗ telephone, the Call Director℗ telephone, the Card Dialer phone, the Touch-Tone telephone, and others. (Courtesy of American Telephone and Telegraph.)

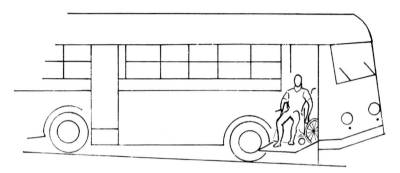

FIGURE 34. Bus with hydraulic lift for wheelchair.

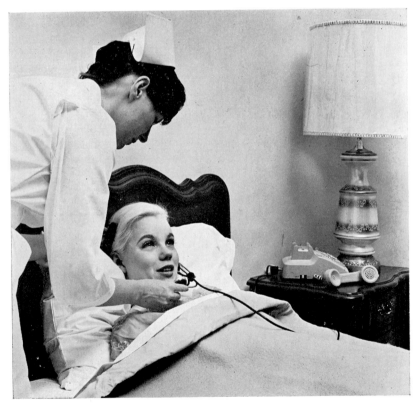

FIGURE 35. A headset, plugged into a jack on the back of a telephone set, brings hands-free telephoning to those who are temporarily or permanently disabled. (Courtesy of American Telephone and Telegraph.)

FIGURE 36. If holding the handset is too tiring, a person may telephone in hands-free ease with the Speakerphone. Just talk into the little desk-top microphone in a conversational tone as if you were talking to your friend face-to-face. You hear his voice coming from the loudspeaker. (Courtesy of American Telephone and Telegraph.)

FIGURE 37. Many youngsters who have to stay home because of a disability can still "go to school" by telephone. Two-way speakers in a classroom and home make this possible. (Courtesy of American Telephone and Telegraph.)

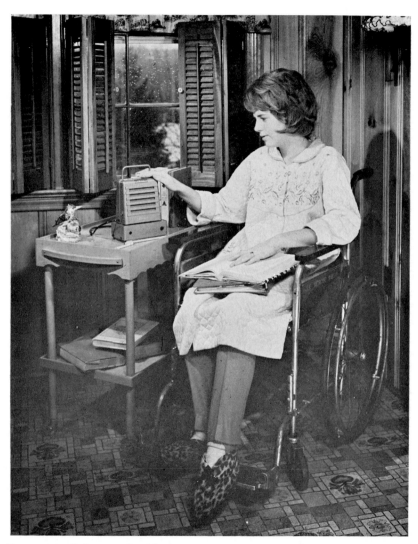

FIGURE 38. Going to school by phone. (Courtesy of American Telephone and Telegraph.)

FIGURE 39. Special device for dialing. Joint research project by Bell System and Institute of Rehabilitation Medicine aims to find out which kind of telephone equipment best meets the needs of patients with each of the major types of motion handicap. Here Joy Cordery, OTR, conducts tests in which quadriplegic patient attempts to dial with special dialing device. G. M. Smith of A.T. and T. engineering looks on. (Courtesy of American Telephone and Telegraph.)

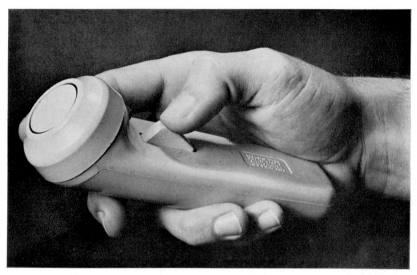

FIGURE 40. This is the Bell System electronic larynx built by Western Electric. There is a low-frequency model for men and a higher-pitched model for women. The thumb control enables the user to vary the inflection of his voice to avoid a monotonous or mechanical sound. (Courtesy of American Telephone and Telegraph.)

FIGURE 41. Flashing lights instead of telephone bell. An ordinary lamp, plugged into the signal control unit at the lower right, becomes a visual attention-getter to let a deaf person know that someone is trying to reach him by telephone. The light flashes on each time the telephone rings. People with normal hearing use a visual signal instead of a bell in order to receive telephone calls late at night without disturbing other members of the household. (Courtesy of American Telephone and Telegraph.)

Chapter 2

IT'S MADE FOR YOU

The IDEAL HOME is the *made-to-order house*. This is especially true *after* your disability strikes.

Before negotiating for the new, you have your old, inadequate domicile to dispose of. Realizing that whether selling or acquiring real estate, professional help should be sought, you wisely turn to a well-recommended realtor. If you can't decide on one by yourself, contact the local real estate board, which will furnish you with a list of reputable brokers in the community.

Now, instead of having to attend to the multitude of tedious details in finding a buyer—advertising and bargaining, to name only two—you will have an experienced back to bear the burden.

The agent may request you to give him the *exclusive* right to represent you for a sixty-day or ninety-day period. This is customary since it protects the agent's right to commissions regardless of who actually negotiates the sale during the "exclusive" period.

The agreement with the broker should be in writing, specifying (a) the length of time that the "exclusive" right will run and (b) the amount of commissions to be paid the broker.

Commissions vary in different sections. The general amount is 5 per cent of the sale price, although the broker and seller are free to enter into any other terms. It might be well to determine when commission will have been earned: (a) after finding a buyer and signing a contract with him or (b) after actually closing the sale with him and turning over a deed.

You should cooperate fully with the agent. Correct as many defects in the property as possible, as these might deter prospective buyers. Leave the negotiating up to the broker. That's why he's paid a commission.

Knowing that you have a new house in mind, your broker might suggest that you consider a *trade-in*—your old house as part of a deal to secure land upon which to build a new one, or to acquire a home already in existence that may be readily adapted to your requirements. The simplest of this type of transaction is a *straight trade*—merely swapping the old for the new.

Whether selling, buying, trading, or otherwise disposing of real estate, you should be represented by an attorney. With his trained eye in finding flaws in documents, of which there are a vast number in each deal, he will surely save wear and tear on your nervous system and will save perhaps far more in dollars and cents than the fee you pay him. Concerning fees, the amount is agreed in advance between lawyer and client, with the usual cost of services fixed at 1 per cent of the sale price up to $20,000, and calculated on a downward-sliding scale if the price is higher.

Among his functions, your attorney will perform as follows:

1. Study all papers for correctness. (All agreements in real estate transactions should be *in writing*.)

2. Look for prejudicial items in "small print" such as the "escalator clause" often included in mortgages which permit increases in interest rates at the volition of the mortgagee. Banks sometimes exercise the privilege of raising the mortgage interest when interest on deposits is raised. Other reasons for "adjusting the mortgage interest rate" may be set forth in the document, but the only real ceiling is a state's anti-usury law.

   Such clauses are prohibited in mortgages insured by the Veterans Administration or the Federal Housing Administration.

3. Check to see if closing fees and expenses are properly allocated between buyer and seller.

   The seller must pay all taxes and water charges due up to the date of the sale. He must liquidate all debts owed on the premises and pay for Federal tax stamps on the deed.

   The buyer must pay the balance of taxes for the current tax period, the fees for recording the mortgage and deed, and the cost of title search and insurance.

   The parties may agree prior to the closing, *in writing,* as to other arrangement for the division of such expenses.

As a purchaser, you should study every feature of the deal with extreme care. Because of your disability, each facet of the transaction should be viewed under a mental microscope. If you are under a physician's care, ask his advice as to the climate and altitude best for you, he may also suggest medical facilities available in the area of your choice. As to the latter, the local medical society will be of great assistance.

Before deciding to build, try to find an existing house of the size and nature desired by you. If you are lucky, you will come across one made specifically for someone with a disability similar to yours, with all the refinements required by you and which will readily permit further adaptation to your specific needs.

Barring such a stroke of good fortune, you must acquire a parcel of land and build. This being one of the most important investments in a lifetime, try to leave nothing to chance. Your future happiness at home may depend to a great degree upon the attention paid to minute details at this time.

In choosing a site for building, consider the following:

1. Is the terrain convenient for wheelchair propelling?
2. If you have young children, is there a school nearby?
3. How close are shopping and transportation facilities?
4. Are zoning restrictions of the type to protect the residential nature of the section?
5. What are the location of houses of worship and any other points of importance to *you?*

Suggestions from all sources should be given appropriate heed, especially when offered by your physician, attorney, or real estate broker.

After securing a parcel of land, you should seek a highly recommended builder, one who will be interested in filling your need for a desirable house as well as adding to his bankroll. Your broker may have valuable advice on this score.

If possible, ascertain the financial soundness of a builder before finally selecting him. This knowledge may steer you away from what might become a fiasco. What you want is a well-built, completed home, not a partially completed one stymied by a bankrupt builder.

The architect may be one of your own choice or the builder's. Here again, recommendation by reliable sources is the best method of making a decision. An astute architect will be invaluable in planning a practical home where you will enjoy the many conveniences required by you; the home will also, no doubt, be constructed in a manner to enhance the resale value of the house.

Regardless of the architect's fine reputation, check the finished blueprint yourself for omissions or errors. It is not unheard of, for instance, for the position of the house as reflected in the plans to be reversed from what you desired. Thus, instead of having the pool in a place away from the public eye, the drawings may have it easily visible from the street. Perhaps you wanted the master bedroom to face the cool north, not the torrid west as shown in the plans.

Before finally selecting the architect, it may be advisable to look at some other buildings representative of his work. This will give you an idea of the type of performance you might expect for your job. (Looking at other work of the *builder* might also be a good idea.)

FINANCING

Financing the building is a must. Unless you do it out of your own funds, the usual procedure is to secure a mortgage loan. The builder may arrange for the loan, but it will be your obligation for many years; you should ascertain whether the mortgagee of his selection will prove to be a satisfactory "landlord" to you.

To obtain comparative interest rates and mortgage terms, discuss your situation with the loan officer in different banks. The principal types of such lenders are savings and loan associations, savings banks, and commercial banks.

Factors to be considered in determining the amount of the loan and the number of years for it to run are

1. Your present family income and outlook for the future.
2. Your age, state of health, and size of family.
3. The present amount of your savings and other assets.
4. Your existing debts and obligations.

At the time of paying a deposit to the builder or seller, be sure the contract contains a provision that the transaction is subject to your securing a satisfactory mortgage; otherwise, the deal shall be canceled and the down payment (also called a "binder" or "earnest money") shall be forthwith returned to you. As a precaution, give the payment to the broker who shall hold it in escrow until such time as the contract actually goes into effect, after which he is authorized to turn it over to the builder or seller.

There are three types of mortgages:

1. The "conventional," arranged directly with the lending agency.
2. Federal Housing Administration (F.H.A.), which covers up to 97 per cent of the first $15,000 of the FHA-appraised value plus 90 per cent of the balance.
3. A guaranteed Veterans Administration (V.A.) mortgage.

The F.H.A. and V.A. types of loans are available with small monthly payments and with mortgage periods running as long as thirty years. On the contrary, the conventional mortgage has a relatively short life, thus requiring larger monthly payments.

Eligibility for the V.A.-guaranteed mortgage depends upon the date of the veteran's discharge or separation from the service. Commencing from that time, he may apply within ten years plus one year for each three months of active wartime duty. To be certain of his rights, the veteran should consult with the loan guaranty officer of the local V.A. regional office.

This benefit for World War II veterans terminated July 25, 1967. The cutoff date for Korean veterans is January 31, 1975. There is no foretelling if, when, and how the benefits may be extended.

It is important that your mortgage contain a "prepayment" clause, permitting early repayment of the loan without penalty charges. On the V.A.-guaranteed mortgage, there are no penalties whatsoever for prepayment. Under FHA regulations, prepayment may be made up to 15 per cent of such a loan in any one year without a penalty fee. If the entire FHA mortgage is paid back within ten years, a charge of 1 per cent may be added.

The following, Table I, may assist you in deciding what mortgage suits your purse. It reflects the monthly cost for each $1,000 of the mortgage.

TABLE I

Years of Mortgage	Approximate Rate of Interest				
	5¼%	5½%	5¾%	6%	6½%
20	$6.75	$6.87	$7.03	$7.16	$7.46
25	6.00	6.15	6.30	6.45	6.75
30	5.54	5.68	5.85	6.00	6.32

The approximate total payment over the life of a mortgage of $20,000 is as follows:

	5½%	6%	6½%
20	$33,025.00	$34,416.00	$35,760.00
25	36,900.00	38,700.00	40,500.00
30	40,895.00	43,200.00	45,500.00

For those veterans who can qualify to the satisfaction of the Veterans Administration, there is another benefit that is extremely generous in nature. Under the provisions of Public Law 702 of the 80th Congress, substantial financial assistance has been authorized to qualified veterans, so that they may be enabled to acquire specially adapted housing required by them because of the seriousness of their *service-connected* disability. This law provides as follows:

1. Any veteran who is entitled to compensation from the Veterans Administration for a permanent and total service-connected disability due to spinal cord disease or injury, with paralysis of the legs and lower part of the body, may receive from the V.A. a sum not to exceed $10,000, to obtain land and a housing unit with special facilities made necessary because of the veteran's disability.

For details as to the law and whether you may be entitled to its benefits, you should consult with the real estate officer at the local V.A. regional office.

In building a house under Public Law 702, the V.A. has certain requirements that are mandatory:

1. Doorways should be at least 36 inches wide.
2. Halls should not be less than 48 inches wide.
3. A sheltered passageway should extend from home to garage.
4. Hot water pipes, radiators, and other items that might possibly result in burns or injuries must be concealed or adequately covered.
5. Electric switches and outlets should be from 18 to 48 inches above the floor, within comfortable reach from a wheelchair.
6. Utility controls (circuit-breaker and fuse boxes, thermostats) should be reached easily from a wheelchair.
7. Windows should be operable from a wheelchair.
8. Garage doors should operate by push button or key.

9. A safe ramp for entering or leaving the house must be provided. It should be of a fireproof, nonskid construction, with a gradient of less than 8 degrees, a width of 42 inches or more, and safety railings. (The ideal home has no risers, thus eliminating the need for a ramp.)

10. Bathroom fixtures should be readily and safely accessible. Floors should be nonskid. Grab bars should be sufficient in number and judiciously placed. There should be ample floor space for free wheelchair maneuvering.

These specifications will prove excellent guidelines in building a home for any wheelchair-user, whether the V.A. is involved or not.

After your eligibility has been duly certified by the V.A., you may commit yourself to proceeding with construction. Up to that time, any deposit paid should be on the written understanding that it is fully refundable if the V.A. does not approve of the transaction. Here again, it might be wise to let the broker hold such funds in escrow, subject to the V.A.'s decision.

SPECIFICS ABOUT THE INTERIOR

Now, let's assume you have sold your old house and bought land for the erection of the new one. You have a qualified builder, capable architect, skilled attorney, and a suitable mortgage. A "guardian angel" will not go amiss! Nothing else seems necessary preliminary to getting the job started.

Your architect, in planning the house, will include all details that may add to your safety and comfort. He should consider suggestions from you (who knows your needs better?) and from any other source such as disabled veterans organizations.

In addition to the items required by the V.A., the following should be included:

1. Door sills in the house should be eliminated.
2. Entry doors should open outward for safety (Fig. 12).
3. All rooms should be large enough for easy wheelchair action.
4. Doorways and halls should be ample for wheelchairs (Fig. 13).

The specifications in Table II should be considered when you are planning your home.

TABLE II

Average Wheelchair Specifications

Width when open: 25 inches
Width when folded: 10 inches
Length: 42 inches
Turning space needed for 360 degrees: 5 × 5 feet
Height of seat from floor: 20 inches

Kitchen

Fixtures should be placed in position most convenient for use by you. Appliances which may be included are

1. *Refrigerator and freezer.* A convenient model is a combination, divided lengthwise, with the refrigerator on one side and the freezer on the other.

   Separate units are preferable with the upright freezer being more practical than the chest type. The former takes far less floor space; its contents may be readily seen from a wheelchair; and food, when thoughtfully placed in it, may be effortlessly reached from a sitting position. In the case of a chest freezer, some items must always be on the bottom and inaccessible to one in a wheelchair, unless his arms are of gargantuan length.

   The door should swing away from the work area when possible. These appliances are manufactured with hinges on either the left or right sides. The choice is yours.

   Automatic defrosting is a labor saver. It may be a disadvantage, however, if the house is located in an area subject to violent weather, which may disrupt the electric current if main circuits are exposed to the elements. In such a case, there is always the possibility of the current going off unexpectedly. At a time like that, an accumulation of frost is extremely desirable. If the door is not opened, food within the freezer may be preserved for 48 hours, even if the appliance is not working.

2. *Range.* This item may be operated either by gas or electric. The free-standing type, with cooking surface at counter height and an oven below, is convenient for one in a wheelchair. Wall ovens may be built-in at any desired level.

   The self-cleaning oven, though more expensive than the standard model, is a great saver of energy and is worth the difference in price.

Automatic "controlled" cooking makes things easier for the homemaker; just be certain that the controls are within your reach and that you fully understand how to use them.

3. *Sink.* This appliance may be of standard design. Be sure that faucets can be easily reached from a sitting position and that they have an excellent finish protecting against stains.

There should be no obstructions beneath the sink which would keep the knees from fitting under if this is approached frontally (see *Cabinets* below).

4. *Dishwasher.* Its best position is next to the sink. If the sink can be approached directly from the front, the dishwasher would be to your right if you are right-handed, and to your left if you are left-handed. The front-opener fits beneath a counter of standard height.

These appliances are approximately 24 inches wide, with varying capacities. There is a portable dishwasher of similar width that rolls easily on casters. Its electric wire may be plugged into any standard outlet.

Portables come both in the front-loading and top-loading models. The former, in addition to being more convenient to use from a wheelchair, fits under the average-height counter and may be built-in.

The portable is connected to the sink faucet by a flexible fitting. Waste water goes from dishwasher to sink via a similar tube.

The key to successful use of this homemaker's boon is *hot water*. For best results, its temperature should be about 175 degrees.

5. *Cabinets.* Though actually not appliances, these are integral parts of the kitchen. The shelves should be within easy reach from a seated position and preferably should be the pull-out, adjustable type (Figs. 8 and 14).

Items used frequently should be placed in most convenient positions. Less accessible shelves may be utilized for articles not in daily use.

Doors may be full-sized swinging, hinged in the middle and swinging, sliding, or the accordion type—whichever suits your needs best.

In order to preserve the symmetrical appearance of the kitchen, and yet permitting you to approach the sink directly from the front, a cabinet-type door may be built—even with the others in the room—which, when opened wide, will allow your knees to fit under the sink. This door also may serve to conceal plumbing under the sink and may be used as a place for hanging useful gadgets. A suspended-type garbage can may be hung on the door, thus eliminating a space-taking receptacle from the floor.

4. *Garbage disposal.* This appliance is made part of the sink so that most garbage may be immediately disposed of. When in use, the *cold* water should be running continuously, flushing the garbage down the disposal drain.

   Familiarize yourself with all instructions, as you should do with all appliances. Except for paper, metal objects, and items that might clog the apparatus because of the stringiness of their nature, most garbage may be disposed of in the unit. This is especially appreciated in areas where there is no daily garbage collection by the municipality.

7. *Electric lights, switches, and outlets.* Lighting fixtures should be well placed for maximum illumination without casting shadows. Frosted bulbs or neon tubes do not give harsh glare.

   Switches and outlets should be reached easily. Kitchen work will become easier as you avail yourself of such helpful appliances as electric mixers, blenders, juicers, and toasters. Outlets for the attachment of their plugs should be installed within effortless reach from a seated position.

8. *Washer and dryer.* The combination washer-dryer has certain advantages over the separate items. After putting the wash into the combination, you need do nothing until the laundry is ready to be taken out and stowed away. This type of appliance usually costs less than the total price of an individual washer and dryer. Also, the combination requires only about 25 to 30 inches of floor space, or approximately half of what separate washers and dryers would occupy.

   Automatic washers and dryers come in models operated by both gas and electricity. These machines vary in width from about 28 to 30 inches, with different capacities. The main feature to be considered in deciding which style to purchase is the ease of operation. Other factors are (a) reputation for good service without requiring frequent repairing, (b) adequate size for your family needs, (c) available floor space, and (d) price.

Bathroom

A bathroom usually confronts a wheelchair-user with serious challenges. This room should receive special attention, with great thought being given to the convenient placing of fixtures.

1. *Toilet (also called commode or john).* There are the floor-mounted and wall-hung types. These should be positioned so that one in a wheelchair may approach it in a manner easiest for him. A space of five feet should be adequate to permit a slightly oblique frontal or lateral approach.

   In most instances, the seat height of the commode should be on a level with that of the wheelchair. The height of the wall model is easily controlled by inserting the bracket at the distance above the floor so that, when the fixture is suspended from it, it will be at the desired height (Fig. 15). The standard floor-mounted toilet may have its height increased merely by setting it on a pedestal built for the purpose (Fig. 16).

   The wall-hung type, though perhaps more costly than the floor-mounted one, has certain advantages. It permits closer frontal approach by a wheelchair, and it facilitates floor cleaning all about it.

2. *Basins (also known as sinks).* Whether set in a counter top or bracketed from the wall, there should be no obstruction in front that might prevent a wheelchair occupant from getting his knees beneath. There should be an unobstructed clearance of about 26 inches from the floor to the basin's overhang (Fig. 9).

   Receptacles for soap, toothbrushes, and drinking glasses should be installed within easy reach from a wheelchair. A suggested height from the floor is 42 inches.

Faucets should work easily. They should *not* be the type that turn off automatically.

The medicine chest should be within easy reach, with adjustable shelves. The tilt-out type may be more desirable than the one recessed in the wall. It may be next to the sink if preferred.

The bottom of the bathroom mirror should be no more than 3 feet above the floor.

An electric outlet, within easy reach from a wheelchair, should be in close proximity to the mirror and basin in the event that an electric razor or toothbrush is used.

3. *Shower*. The ride-in type is preferred. Dimensions of 3 × 4 feet are adequate. The overhead spray should have an adjustable, long neck. Sprays on the sides should also be adjustable.

A single control faucet for mixing hot and cold water is recommended.

A folding seat attached to the wall is a convenience. There are wheelchairs that resist ill effect from water,* thus saving you the trouble of changing seats (Fig. 16).

4. *Bathtub*. A wheelchair with footrests that fold back permits close frontal approach to the tub.

A Hoyer Lift is helpful for getting into and out of the tub safely (Fig. 4).

Faucets should be within easy reach from the position in the tub most comfortable for you.

Seats are available specifically for bathtubs. They may be either the stool-type, which rests on the tub's bottom, or the kind which wedges firmly between the insides of the tub (Fig. 5).

Sufficient, well-placed grab rails are musts for safety's sake.

5. *Grab rails (also known as handrails and safety bars)*. These should be placed at all positions in the bathroom and, in fact, anywhere in the house, for your safety and comfort.

Their usual position in the wall is next to the facility to be used. Horizontal rails seem best for pushing yourself in a

---

*Everest and Jennings, Inc., Los Angeles, California.

wheelchair, while vertical rails are best for pulling. When in a diagonal position, they may serve both purposes.

There should be a clearance of about 1½ inches from bar to wall. Bars should have a nonslip finish. There is a bar made especially for bathtubs, which fits over the side. Bars may also serve as places to hang towels or laundry items for drying (Figs. 5, 6, 17 and 18).

Living Room

This room should be furnished with the wheelchair-user uppermost in mind. Like the other rooms, it should not be cluttered, and the conventional appearance should be maintained.

Cushions on sofas and upholstered chairs, firm in nature, are most convenient. Chair and sofa heights may be increased by placing wooden blocks beneath the legs.

A desk or writing table should have ample knee room. An adjustable lamp suspended from a wall, within easy reach from a sitting position, will provide necessary illumination without occupying any of the writing surface. There should be generous drawer space so that everything you need may be close at hand. One drawer large enough to hold letter files may come in handy. End tables with room for books and sundry items are advisable.

A coffee table with shelves and drawers on easy rolling castors will be a great convenience when entertaining guests. Coasters for drinking glasses, ice tongs, a cork screw, playing cards, and numerous other miscellaneous items will be close at hand when needed.

Smooth, unwaxed floor covering is better than carpeting. Scatter rugs should be shunned.

Dining Area

Whether it is part of another room such as an L-shaped offshoot of the living room or whether it is a full-sized dining room, the dining area should not be crowded with furniture.

The essentials are a table and four or six chairs. If additional seating is needed, folding chairs will prove excellent. They require less floor space than standard chairs and may be easily stored when not in use. The ideal table is the extension type that, at its smallest, is about the size of an average card table yet opens to accommodate as many as sixteen diners.

The dining area should adjoin or be as close as possible to the kitchen. This will reduce to a minimum the distance traversed in serving and clearing the table. In this respect, a small table on freely rolling wheels will be most helpful.

If there is a partition between the kitchen and dining space, a pass-through with a broad counter will be advantageous. Dishes and food may be conveyed easily through this opening. The counter may also be a perfect position for a telephone which can be comfortably utilized in both rooms.

Well-placed electric outlets should be installed so that appliances such as toasters and electric percolators may be used at the table.

Bedroom

This room should be uncluttered and large enough to permit a wheelchair to move about freely, without difficult maneuvering. To provide a maximum of floor space, the number of articles of furniture should be only the number actually needed.

A large walk-in closet may be set up in a manner which will obviate the need of dressers by having bins built on the shelves that serve to neatly hold shirts, underwear, handkerchiefs, socks, and other items customarily found in bureau drawers (Fig. 7).

The indispensable piece of furniture which deserves great consideration in its selection is the bed. It should be of strong construction and of a size adequate to assure your comfort.

Beds come in several sizes; the huge king size (72 × 80 in), the queen size (60 × 80 in), the double bed (54 × 75 in), and the twin bed (38 × 75 in).

For most individuals who have difficulty turning in bed, the twin size is most practical. It provides ample sleeping area and is narrow enough so that an occupant may reach and grip the mattress edges for added leverage when desiring a change of position.

The bed, with mattress, should be approximately the same height as the wheelchair seat. There should be at least 10 inches of clearance from the floor on the sides of the bed to permit the footrests of the chair to fit under the bed—if that is how you approach it.

The height of the bed may be changed to suit your requirements by selecting a mattress of suitable thickness, by placing wooden blocks beneath the legs, or by installing castors. The latter should be equipped with brakes for safety.

A Gatch Spring, as usually used in hospital beds, enables the height to be varied and permits changes in the spring's level because of hinged joints. The Gatch type may fit in the standard frame, and it operates automatically (electrically) or manually (by use of cranks).

The headboard may have grab bars or spindles attached to it to assist the occupant in moving and turning over.

Great consideration should be given in selecting a mattress. There are three principal types: the foam rubber, which comes in various thicknesses and degrees of firmness; the solid upholstered; and the upholstered innerspring.

The latter variety of mattress is most popular. If possible, you should test it for comfort by actually lying on it. The borders should have reinforced padding covered by ticking. There should be air vents so that the mattress may "breathe," and there should be firmly attached handles.

If you find that the mattress "gives" too much, a wooden board may be placed between it and the spring. This board, usually made of plywood, may be hinged so as to accommodate adjustments permitted by the Gatch Spring.

Although bed linens are usually taken for granted, their selection should be given thought. The most durable materials are muslin and percale. Although muslin is more reasonable in price, percale is of a finer quality, making for a comparatively luxurious sleep. Contoured bottom sheets with elasticized corners prove best in bed making. The top sheet should be the standard type.

Nylon or other extremely slippery materials are not recommended for sheeting. No matter how well they are tucked under the mattress, the slightest pull will cause them to slide out. What may have been a fine surface to rest upon will thus become an ocean of wrinkles.

An important adjunct to the bed is a night table with roomy drawers and easily reached shelves. This table should have a surface broad enough to hold a telephone, books, signal device, and anything else for your convenience in bed.

To complete the bedroom furnishing, you may wish to have a chair of the conventional types as a change from the wheelchair. Your selection should be of strong construction with a solid base so that it will be difficult to tip over.

A large mirror should be included in the decor. A bed lamp may be attached to the headboard or hung from the wall behind the bed. The light switch should be installed within easy reach.

Garage or Carport

This part of the house is of major importance. Here your great ally, the automobile, is housed. Your garage or carport should be oversized so that when you are seated in a wheelchair, you will be able to get around the car even when the door is closed.

The door should be the type that slides overhead and operates automatically by use of a conveniently placed push button in the garage and a key switch attached to a post or other easily reached position outside. You should be able to insert the key in the switch merely by extending your arm through a car window. Ultrasonic devices which permit operation of the door from within the vehicle are available at a somewhat higher cost. Manual operation of the door should be possible in case the current goes off.

As a wheelchair-user shuns stairs, your house will probably not have an attic or cellar. The garage may serve as a storeroom, laundry room, and place for the hot water heater.

The garage should be attached to the house, with an entrance directly into the house. This is a great convenience, especially when weather is inclement and when articles are to be brought to or from the car.

Any incline into the garage should be less than 5 degrees to serve as an easily managed ramp.

Although a carport may serve the purpose of sheltering your car and is less costly to build than the closed garage, there is no denying the latter being preferable. A locked door offers better security not only from the elements but also against theft and vandalism.

Termite-proofing

During the course of construction from beginning to end, every part of your structure should be treated to repel and destroy such insects as termites and carpenter ants, which can gnaw away at wooden parts of the house until beams and studs are no longer strong enough to support the building.

SPECIFICS ABOUT THE EXTERIOR

Patio or Porch

These places of relaxation should be screened to keep out pesky insects, curious dogs and miscellaneous uninvited "guests," and flying leaves and debris. Fiber-glass screening is suggested since it does not corrode, does an excellent job, and is very economically-priced (Fig. 4).

Pool

This will add to your enjoyment of the house, will serve as a method to secure water therapy if such is desired, and will enhance the property value.

Although not as exotic-looking as the kidney-shaped type, the rectangular pool provides more swimming area.

For added security, a rail should be installed on the inside of the pool just above the water line. This position will minimize rusting from contact with pool water if the rail is metal.

To facilitate getting into and out of the pool by one confined to a wheelchair, a ramp may be constructed so that the chair may ride into the water. The ramp should not be too steep.

The hydraulic-operated Hoyer Lift may be more satisfactory than the ramp. It is embedded at the pool's edge and requires only a few inches of space. A practical ramp may need many feet of space for a gradual slope (Fig. 4).

Landscaping

Employing a professional to do the work will relieve you of many problems but will be more costly than if you did the work. However, the nature of the results of a skilled landscape architect may be well worth the extra expense.

If *you* decide to be the artist, give prime consideration to ease of maintenance. If taking care of lawns is not feasible, the endless ritual of cutting grass may be reduced by having most of the grounds occupied by flower beds, shrubs, and trees. Slow growers need less-frequent trimming.

A built-in sprinkler system for watering will facilitate gardening.

In selecting foliage, select plants that will add to the property value. The house may be a beauty, so don't let the "frame" detract from the picture.

So that you have access to all parts of the property, smooth-surfaced cement walks should be provided. A width of 44 inches will comfortably accommodate a wheelchair. The surface of the walks should be "pock marked" to reduce slipperiness. This safety feature can be created by jabbing the wet concrete with the bristles of a broom.

FINAL WORDS ABOUT YOUR NEW HOME

1. See Figures 19 and 20 for suggested layouts.
2. An intercom system connected with the front entrance will permit you to "screen" callers from your desk, for example, without the effort of going to the door. A push-button opener will enable you to admit desirable visitors easily, despite your being far from entry.
3. A *built-in vacuum cleaner system* is an energy saver. The only necessary equipment is a flexible hose with various attachments. Wall outlets for the hose should be strategically placed.
4. An exhaust fan above the range will draw off heat and cooking odors.
5. Conveniently placed racks for cloth towels and paper products along with a built-in broom closet, are desirable in the kitchen.
6. To reduce strenuous stretching, reaching tongs and a long-handled brush and dust pan should be readily available.
7. *Door knobs* should have a nonslip finish and should be easily reached from a wheelchair.
8. *Door sills* inside the house should be eliminated. Slightly raised entry sills may be unavoidable. By placing flexible tubing along the edges that will compress under weight, the rise will become negligible as a wheelchair rolls over it.

9. *Doors* may be the conventional hinged type, the accordion model, or the slide-within-the-wall. Sliding *glass* doors, when closed, should be made as conspicuous as possible. To prevent anyone from crashing through, these doors should contain a surface etching or a clearly visible decal at a height easily seen by both children and adults. For best protection against broken, jagged glass that can be quite deadly, shatter-proof glass should be used.

   Plastic kick plates, fastened at a proper height will prevent wooden doors from being marred by constant contact with footrests.

10. The central type of air-conditioning with reversible cycle for heating is unbeatable. Operation may be by gas or electric. The thermostat control should be the style that automatically changes from cooling to heating and vice versa according to the temparture.

11. *Circuit breakers* are preferable to fuses. Instead of having to replace a burned out fuse to restore interrupted current, a flip of a switch in the circuit-breaker box will do the trick. These boxes should be within easy reach from a wheelchair.

12. *Window sills* made of marble or ceramic tiles are easiest to keep clean.

    To see over them from a sitting position, sills should be approximately three feet from the floor.

13. Traverse *draperies* that cover the entire window are attractive and afford great privacy. They hang from a special track installed near the ceiling, with the cord controlling the operation conveniently placed.

    For very bright exposures, you may find an opaque lining on a separate track extremely helpful.

14. *Window shades and blinds* should be carefully selected. The roller-type shade comes in many attractive designs and offers all necessary privacy with easy maintenance.

    Blinds of the slatted variety are difficult to take care of and are not recommended.

With your new home completed, you anxiously look forward to moving in. This usually is a complicated operation; however with astute planning, it can be almost "painless."

MOVING

Select a mover who is highly recommended, with a reputation for quality service.

Having the movers do the packing will make for efficient, safe transporting of your property. All you will have to do is prepare the articles for packing. Depending upon the size of the job, the packers will go to work readying things for the move anytime from 24 hours to a week before M-day. Fragile items will be carefully wrapped. Specially designed cartons will be employed. Everything will be accorded a maximum of protection so that the odds are in your favor that everything will arrive intact at the destination. However, get full property insurance "just in case."

If *you* decide to do the packing, give yourself plenty of time. For fragile articles, secure containers from your mover; the ones he uses are of reinforced construction and can safely withstand the vicissitudes of moving. Plenty of crumpled paper should be placed on the bottoms of barrels to act as shock absorbers. Books and other nonbreakable items may be packed in boxes supplied by your grocer. Phonograph records should be packed upright to minimize the possibility of warping. Furniture drawers may be utilized for linens and bedding.

It might be well to let the mover pack delicate articles. Their preservation may justify the added cost. Also, in such case, the mover will be responsible for any damage.

Make a careful inventory of all items involved; number the containers in sequence. Indicate on each container the room in the new house where you desire it to be placed. Furniture may be similarly labeled.

Cost is always a consideration in selecting a mover, although it should be secondary to his reputation. Get a price estimate in advance. Rates vary according to weight if the move is interstate; for nonlocal intrastate, a combination of weight and distance controls the cost; for purely local moves, the prevailing hourly charge is the determining factor. One way to reduce the moving expense is *not* to take things you really do not need. It way be more economical to buy new pieces at your destination rather than moving the old. This may be the perfect time to get rid of anything useless or obsolete.

For a smooth-operating move, you should:

1. Arrange for insurance covering all possible losses during the moving, and secure a comprehensive homeowner's policy for the new house.
2. Obtain references for medical and dental services at the new locale.
3. Notify organizations and publishers which send you mail of the address change about six weeks in advance of the move.
4. About a month prior to the move, advise friends, stores where you have charge accounts, delivery people (newspaper, milk), and any governmental agencies with which you may be concerned.
5. Arrange for utilities at the new location.
6. Return all borrowed items such as library books.
7. Notify the post office of change of address about a week in advance.
8. If travel and overnight stops are involved in the move, make timely arrangements and reservations.
9. If you will travel by car, have your vehicle put in tip-top condition.
10. If moving involves changing schools for children, take necessary records.

Chapter 3

— ARCHITECTS AND BUILDERS, THANKS —
OFF LIMITS NO LONGER!

Mᴏʀᴇ ᴛʜᴀɴ ᴀ quarter of a million Americans are in wheelchairs, and many persons have some other disability which makes entering and leaving the average building a major problem. Research has provided us with some of the standards to make buildings and facilities more accessible to the handicapped. We now must put this information to practical use by eliminating architectural barriers from existing buildings, and preventing them in the vast amount of public and private construction which lies ahead."

On April 26, 1966, President Lyndon B. Johnson spoke these words. At that time he appointed the National Commission on Architectural Barriers, whose function was to determine the extent to which structural barriers impede access to, or the use of, facilities in various types of edifices. The commission's duty thereafter was to make recommendations regarding the action necessary to permit the disabled to make full use of such buildings.

This event was one of the recent links in the chain which will eventually culminate with structures to accommodate *all*. What is convenient for a wheelchair-user will benefit the general public, disabled or not.

The subject of architectural barriers has been a problem from time immemorial. It was updated with a bang in May of 1957 when President Eisenhower was to present a trophy to a man named the Handicapped American of the Year. When the honored guest reached the building where the ceremonies were to take place, he was barred from entry—by a multitude of steps! He was in a wheelchair. It required two marines to carry him into the auditorium. It hardly needs saying that this unfortunate episode led to a ramp being constructed for the benefit of *future* nonambulatory visitors.

Over the ensuing years, from May 1959 when the President's Committee on Employment of the Handicapped first met to discuss the matter of barriers, a series of other committees held successive meetings, resulting in what is known as American Standard Specifications, approved on October 31, 1961 by the powers that be. These specifications were applicable to facilities in public buildings, industry, education, recreation, and to other sites where architectural barriers would reduce or prevent normal enjoyment of such places by the disabled.

With general acceptance in industry, the wheelchair-bound individual is for all practical purposes, on a par with his able-bodied brethren—except when confronted by vexatious restrictions because of structural impediments. Soon, let's succeed in knocking down these frustrating "Walls of Jericho," created by thoughtlessness.

In planning a structure, the builder or architect needs only to suppose that he were seriously disabled—one of that ever-growing segment of our population who desires nothing except to get to work at his regular employment, to visit museums and other cultural exhibits, to vote by personal appearance at the polling place rather than by absentee ballot, to attend religious services, to enjoy sports and other forms of entertainment, to. . . . This list of things that the seriously disabled person must participate in in order to stay in the mainstream of life could be multiplied manyfold.

Even after the "sacrosanct" obstacle of steps has been done away with on the exterior of a building, there remains another obstacle course: free access to all facilities *within* the building is essential. Narrow halls and doors may make navigating from place to place on the job difficult. Inaccessible restrooms may make employment on the premises impossible, no matter how well-suited you are for the position. If drinking fountains are not reachable from a wheelchair, you can't quench a normal thirst. Here again, the number of stumbling blocks to the disabled is endless.

Although fighting for the right to earn a living is a principal part of the disabled person's everyday life, he tries for the well-rounded existence. Why shouldn't he be an active participant in community affairs without requiring assistance from others to enter or leave public structures, or even to use a telephone?

Now that a giant step has been taken in formulating structural specifications that will set a safe, sensible standard of construction directed at benefiting the disabled, it is up to builders, architects, and engineers, as well as all other interested parties, to see to it that these building reforms become a reality. Let the deed reflect the vast volume of words. As a bettor would say, "Put your money where your mouth is."

With so many buildings in existence that have a lack of interior conveniences required by the severely disabled, and whose outsides resemble Greek temples because of heaven-reaching flights of stairs, immediate attention should be given to make suitable alterations in these structures to meet the needs of those with infirmities.

Such adaptation is often not possible or is extremely difficult and costly. However, if any substantial improvement can be made, the end will surely justify the means.

Many individuals once prevented from earning a livelihood because of industrial "physical disabilities" will return to the ranks of income earners. This will cause a beneficial chain reaction: a new group of taxpayers will be established; these workers will have money to spend on luxuries as well as necessities, thus putting more money in circulation; by being able to enter polling places, the disabled will be permitted to exercise their civic duty of voting; accessible public buildings will result in their participating in community affairs. The fact is that by aiding the disabled "to get back on their feet," the nation will benefit socially and economically.

Since the program for the improvement of physical aspects of buildings has come into effect, many old ones have had a face-lifting, so that storming their walls is no longer a formidable challenge to the disabled. The effect goes beyond industry. Houses of worship, where *all* may enter, are rewarded by substantial increases in the sizes of their congregations, both disabled and able-bodied. Places of entertainment show a similar beneficial result. Accessible libraries and museums are frequented by many of those persons once barred from their facilities.

President Kennedy, in pushing for accelerated action with respect to improved construction, wrote: ". . . Yet we must remember that standards remain nothing more than words and phrases unless they are translated into action. To serve the purpose for which they are created, they must be adopted. They must be put into use in designing new public buildings and in remodeling old. . . ."

". . . I can further assure you that the agencies and departments of the Federal Government that come under the jurisdiction of my Office will give full support to this worthy project."

It is encouraging to see how the specifications of the American Standards Committee are being implemented in construction throughout the country. The ultimate goal is to have these standards, improved and augmented by new and even better ones, put into effect in every new structure, with existing ones modified accordingly wherever feasible.

As a result, the seriously disabled, who, though welcomed are paradoxically often excluded by structural shortcomings, will find themselves active participants in life's mainstream instead of merely being spectators, unhappy and chagrined. To them, the unadorned ramp, automatically operated doors (Fig. 21), and nonslip floors are far more glorious than the most imposing flight of steps, the most beautiful and intricately designed doors which seem to weigh a ton, or the most highly polished floors that gleam from a waxed finish.

By rehabilitating old buildings and thoughtfully planning new ones, many of the disabled formerly relegated to institutions and "back-room living," protected, pampered, and sometimes hidden by family and friends, will eagerly venture forth in an attempt to rejoin society.

One of the saddest aspects resulting from architectural barriers is that numerous disabled persons, contrary to the facts, convince themselves that they would be better off to "step aside." They do not want to be continuous burdens on others, with the humiliating dread of becoming entirely dependent on society thus relinquishing sovereignty over their own lives.

Facing reality, in many instances they have become a burden in their endeavor to project themselves into a normal way of life. But they are not basically at fault: the blame rests upon the heads of those apathetic to the problems of the disabled.

At long last, all that indifference seems headed for the junk yard of oblivion. Society has stepped in to lend a firm hand, with a desire to restore the disabled to usefulness to themselves and the community.

Perhaps some of this new interest in breaking down structural barriers came about from a realization, after mature thought, that among the disabled was a vast, much-needed store of artistic and scientific talent. Whatever the reason, selfish or otherwise, the desired result is in view: complete independence for the disabled. How important this has become!

In this era of scientific and medical advances, machines are maiming and killing in every direction. Add to this those with spinal cord injuries and diseases, severe arthritics, serious coronary cases, those who have sustained accidental injuries with permanent or temporary disability, and those in the ever-mounting ranks of war casualties.

Once the fate of so many of this group was to remain in seclusion "behind the woodwork." Now the pendulum is swinging in their favor. With improvement in physical rehabilitation and increased longevity, environmental problems must receive prime attention. Structural "disabilities" must go!

For a list of standards as established by the American Standards Association, that organization may be contacted at 10 East 40th Street, New York, New York.

These standards are presented for voluntary use by all who are desirous of improving facilities in buildings so that they are accessible to, and usable by, the physically disabled. The essential elements of the specifications, as standardized, are contained in Table III.

TABLE III

RECOMMENDED STANDARDS.

These apply to public buildings, not private residences.

1. *Wheelchair facts.* The following must be considered:
    a. For a turn of 360 degrees, a minimum of 54 inches is required. A space of at least 56 × 63 inches is desirable for the average chair.
    b. Average wheelchair dimensions.
        (1) Length—42 inches
        (2) Width—25 inches (open), 11 inches (folded).
        (3) Height of pusher handles from floor—36 inches.
        (4) Height of seat from floor—20 inches.
    c. Average adult reach from a wheelchair.
        (1) Vertically—60 inches.
        (2) Horizontally—30 inches.
        (3) Diagonally—48 inches from the floor.
2. *Building site.* There should be at least one ground-level entrance. This may require grading of the land.
3. *Area walks*
    a. Should have a nonslip surface.

    b. Average width—48 inches.

    c. Grade—less than 5 degrees.

    d. Long or graded walks should have level surfaces at intervals for rest and safety.

    e. Intersecting walks should meet at the same level.

    f. If a door swings onto a walk, there should be a level space for its safe clearance of at least 5 × 5 feet. If the door does not swing toward the walk, a level platform 3 feet deep by 5 feet wide is adequate.

        (1) The platform should extend at least 1 foot beyond each side of the doorway.

4. *Vehicular parking spaces.* These should be established as close as possible to the facility.

    a. Terrain should be smooth and level for safe use by wheelchair occupants.

    b. Each parking space should be about 12 feet wide.

    c. Parking lots should be constructed so as to avoid the necessity of patrons having to wheel behind other parked cars.

    d. Spaces created for the use of disabled should be clearly identified and reserved for their exclusive use (Fig. 22).

5. *Ramps.* These should replace steps when feasible.

    a. Their slope should not exceed a rise of 1 foot in 12 feet, or 8 degrees.

    b. Handrails on both sides are desirable, although a rail on one side is adequate. Rails should be about 32 inches above the ramp (Figs. 23 and 24).

    c. The ramp surface should be nonslip.

        (1) A simple way to accomplish this is to pock-mark the ramp. If it is made of cement, the bristles of a broom jabbed into the wet concrete will do the trick. Wooden ramps may be roughened by ordinary carpenter's tools, very coarse sandpaper, or sand sprinkled on wet-paint surface.

    d. There should be no less than 6 feet of level clearance at the bottom; if the ramp is very long there should be level platforms at intervals of 25 to 30 feet for rest and safety.

        (1) There should also be level platforms at the top, similar to specification 3 (f) above, relating to *walks.*

6. *Doors.* These recommendations apply to exterior and interior doorways.

    a. Door clearance should be at least 32 inches.

    b. Two-leaf doors are not convenient and should be avoided unless they may be operated easily by a single effort.

    c. Automatically operated doors are excellent.

    d. Time-delay closers are suggested.

    e. Long bars instead of knobs for pulling doors are very helpful.

    f. If doors swing inward and out, visibility should be permitted on both sides.

    g. Revolving doors are not usable by many persons.

    h. All major egress doors should swing out with slight pressure on the release lever.

        (1) This mechanism is also known as a "panic bar."

    i. Kick plates of a protective material should be attached to the bottom part of the door to protect it from abuse by contact with wheelchair footrests.

    j. Door sills should be level with the floor whenever possible.

    k. The floor should be level for at least 5 feet from the door in the direction that it swings and should extend a foot beyond each side of the door.

    l. Door checks should be selected, set, and installed with great care, so that they will not make the door "too heavy" for use by the disabled.

7. *Floors*

    a. Surface should be nonslip.

     b. Floors on any given story should be on the same level or connected by a ramp.
       (1) See 5 above for *Ramp* specifications.

8. *Restrooms (toilet facilities).* These should be sufficient in number and usable by wheelchair occupants.
     a. At least one stall should be 3 feet wide and 5 feet deep, or larger.
     b. Seat should be at least 20 inches from the floor.
     c. Grip rails, running horizontally 33 inches above the floor, should be fastened firmly on each side of the commode.
       (1) There should be $1\frac{1}{2}$ inches clearance between the wall and rail.
     d. If the stall has a door, it should be at least 33 inches wide and should swing outward.
     e. A wall-mounted commode with a narrow understructure will permit a wheelchair occupant to approach it closely and is most desirable.
       (1) Also enables cleaning beneath the bowl, resulting in better sanitary conditions.
     f. The floor-mounted "john" should be shallow in the front in such a manner as to allow close approach by one in a wheelchair.
     g. Wash basins should have no obstructions beneath so that a wheelchair-user's knees may fit under.
     h. Mirrors, shelves, towel racks, and soap dishes should be no more than 40 inches above the floor.
     i. Drainpipes and hot water pipes should be covered to prevent those who may touch them from being burned.

9. *Water fountains.* There should be an adequate number of these on each floor, conveniently placed for easy use by the disabled.
     a. These should be hand operated, with spouts and controls up front.
     b. Fully recessed coolers are not recommended, nor are fountains set in alcoves—unless the alcove is wide enough for a wheelchair.

10. *Public telephones.* See Chapter 8 on telephones.
     a. There should be an adequate number of phones on each floor, and all should be easily usable by wheelchair occupants.
       (1) The dial and handset should be low enough for convenient use.
       (2) Booths should be wide enough to admit a wheelchair, or at least to permit close approach by its occupant.
       (3) Special problems should be discussed with the telephone company, which will cooperate to the maximum so that all may readily use the telephone equipment.

11. *Elevators.* These are necessary in multi-story structures.
     a. These should be easily accessible from entry by a wheelchair-user and ample in size.
     b. Controls should be within reach of one seated in a wheelchair.
     c. In addition to an emergency alarm button, a telephone inside the elevator is an added security factor.

12. *Switches and controls.* These, in general, include lights, thermostats, alarms, windows, and draperies.
     a. All should be easily reached and operated by one seated in a wheelchair.

13. *Hazards.* Effort should be made to obviate them.
     a. Openings in floors and pavement should be avoided.
     b. Low-hanging signs and lighting fixtures should be eliminated.
       (1) No objects should protrude into trafficked areas or corridors in regular use unless they are at least $6\frac{1}{2}$ feet above the floor.
     c. Grilled radiators are recommended to prevent burns resulting from contact with such a heating device.

14. *Lighting.* Should be ample to illuminate all work areas adequately.
     a. Ramps and walks should be well illuminated.
     b. Exit signs should be clearly visible.

The specifications discussed in Table III will rarely cause an increase in the construction cost and may be made in existing buildings at only a small expense. Certainly the benefits that will accrue to disabled persons occupied in the structure from the standpoint of safety and comfort will more than justify the extra cost. Productivity will be increased, as will safety. Accidents will be reduced, resulting in lower insurance rates.

The implementation of the American standards, as they exist at present (and will surely be revised from time to time because of technological advances), will benefit society as a whole. The prime recipients will be those with problems involving ambulation, coordination, old age, and deficiencies in sight and hearing. What a giant step will have been taken when all persons affected by these problems are "at home" on the job, visiting public places such as museums and libraries, exercising their rights to vote, entering court houses, or even securing dog licenses! (See Figs. 25, 26, and 27.)

Although originally established to directly benefit those with walking problems, the guidelines fostered by the American Standards Association, when incorporated in structural designs, helped a much wider segment of the population. To mention only a few categories, there are the cardiacs with very limited ability to ambulate, those with temporary impairments to their ability to walk, pregnant women, and those pushing baby carriages. Yes, level or ramped entrances, wide doorways, and adequate elevators are boons to hundreds of thousands.

It is interesting to note that more than twenty states have enacted some legislation directed at eliminating architectural barriers from structures erected with public funds. On the Federal level, contractors dealing with the National government have as one of the requirements in every Federal building that there be at least one entrance easily accessible to wheelchair occupants.

The concept of building for the "average" person has gone to its "happy hunting grounds." We now realize that the "average" individual is only a small percentage of the population. Why should the large number of "nonaverage" be prejudiced by faultily designed buildings? Society has made a decision. If man can be put into orbit at a fabulous cost, he certainly should have no difficulty in finding his way into his place of business, church, or theater. In this respect, research has come back to earth.

There are many cases which might be cited where laudatory action has been taken by subdivisions of the government to eliminate architectural barriers. One of the best specific examples is what has been done in Nassau County in New York State.

The County Executive, Hon. Eugene H. Nickerson, organized a committee in November of 1963 which was concerned with improving county facilities in behalf of disabled persons. This included making old public buildings accessible to those with infirmities and establishing a code for new buildings that would assure the absence of such barriers in new structures.

As a result, it was decided that all future county public buildings, whether in the course of construction or in the planning stage, be built without architectural barriers for wheelchair-users and other disabled persons.

Accordingly, specifications were given with respect to facilities in which the disabled were most often affected. These included most of those specifications set up by the American Standards Committee (Table III).

In addition, several buildings in Nassau County were modified, or are in the process of being modified, to meet the needs of such disabled individuals.

1. *Tackapausha Museum*—This is to be provided with all facilities required by the disabled, including convenient, adequate parking spaces.
2. *County Executive Building*—All facilities are to be incorporated in the existing structure, including improved restrooms and new ramps for easier access.
3. *Family Court Buildings*—Full facilities are to be provided.
4. *Administration Building*—The type of construction to provide satisfactory structural details is under careful study by the Department of Public Works.
5. *Hicksville Public Library Annex*—Plans for this building were modified to include an entrance ramp for use by the physically disabled.
6. *Salisbury Park*—The committee recommended strategically

placed ramps, a large and more adequate area for parking, and important changes in restrooms, making the facilities usable for wheelchair-users and disabled persons in general.

Similar modifications have been made in the Park Club House so that restrooms and the main-floor dining rooms are accessible.

In addition to planning and building adequate new structures and altering existing ones so that they are usable by the disabled, the Nassau County Committee on the Handicapped has contacted the Long Island Builders Institute to interest its members in providing more accessible buildings. Emphasis has been placed on the ease of adapting existing structures to accommodate the disabled.

An interesting method of combating architectural barriers was inaugurated by the American Institute of Architects in Kansas City. It involved the direct, person-to-person approach to those deeply concerned with improving opportunities for disabled persons.

The grass-roots program was started by discussions with architects. First, as many architectural barriers as could be thought of were identified. After the existence of the problem had been implanted, it seemed that plans thereafter made many provisions for the benefit of the handicapped. The "worksheet" established to aid participants in the project reads:

"1. *The Problem.* Over 20 million physically disabled persons in the United States are being deprived of the opportunity to participate in community life because of conditions in public buildings which prevent independent access and use of these buildings.

2. *With What Are We Concerned?* Making it possible for the talents and resources of physically handicapped individuals to be realized.

3. *With Whom Are We Concerned?*
    a. The nonambulatory. People in wheelchairs.
    b. The semiambulatory. . . ."

It went on to specify other classes of the disabled: those with impaired sight and hearing, incoordinates, and the aged. Then a list of types of buildings with their locations was compiled. Included were (a) governmental, industrial, office and apartment buildings, (b) restaurants, (c) educational, medical and religious structures, and (d) recreational facilities.

Each participating member of the Inventory Committee chose a representative number of buildings in each category and then plunged into the fieldwork to uncover barriers that could be corrected and to make recommendations. The goal of this orderly survey, as set forth by the "Architectural Opportunity for All" group conducting the research, was "to determine what we are talking about."

At the conclusion of this investigation, many persons prominent in the architectural profession were astonished by learning how many places were "booby trapped" against the disabled because of structural barriers.

An encouraging decision was reached. With the united action of architects, engineers, designers, builders, manufacturers, and legislators, and with serious coordinated planning, such structures will be erected and old ones so-modified as to open up new worlds to millions of individuals whose horizons have been reduced by thoughtlessness. The imaginary sign, "Handicapped, Keep Out," has been recognized and is fading into oblivion.

For the convenience of disabled visitors, many communities have published information setting forth places that are easily accessible. *New York With Ease* is one such publication. It may be secured at the Easter Seal Society, 239 Park Avenue South, New York, New York.

This booklet compactly lists many amenities in New York City, with details of their physical aspects that would interest the disabled. The city is divided into its boroughs, and many points of interest in each area are stated.

In the Table of Contents of this book, the following are designated: restaurants, theaters, motion-picture houses, museums, art galleries, music, libraries, shopping, beauty salons, bowling, and hotels.

The information given includes cost and specifics about steps, width of doors, elevator facilities, availability of assistance, accessibility of restrooms, and ramps. It also tells whether a spectator may remain in his wheelchair in a theater or must transfer to a seat and other interesting facts.

It is advisable to check with local chambers of commerce and tourist bureaus for details of accessible amenities. These organizations will cooperate to the maximum. Just state your requirements—physical, financial, and otherwise.

On the Federal level, information may be secured concerning monuments, national parks, and other points of interest in the United States convenient for visitation by the disabled by writing the President's Committee on Employment of the Handicapped, Washington, D.C.

Although most of our parks are suitable for the physically fit who are able to hike, climb, and ride horseback, there is no reason why the disabled are barred in many instances from enjoying museums, exhibits, cabins, restaurants, restrooms, and other facilities separate from the rugged terrain.

It would be unreasonable to ask that the parks be made over for use by the disabled, but there is no reason for there being steps leading to them, or doorways being too narrow for wheelchairs.

Fortunately, this sad situation is being corrected as fast as reasonably possible. The director of the National Park Service has instructed his service to "adopt at once an architectural code that will, in the future, make all public buildings erected in the parks usable by the handicapped. . . ."

As important as it is for these public facilities to be usable by the disabled, it is equally important for their whereabouts to be known. An extremely comprehensive booklet, published by the President's Committee in cooperation with the Veterans Employment Service of the U.S. Department of Labor Manpower Administration, is entitled *Guide to the National Parks and Monuments for Handicapped Tourists.*

It divides the country into different sections and itemizes places of tourist interest in each, giving information of special interest to the disabled. One example is the Thomas Jefferson Memorial, Washington, D.C.:

> . . . Many steps leading up to the interior of the monument make it inaccessible for persons in wheelchairs. . . . No special facilities are provided for the handicapped. However, the guards will assist handicapped persons if requested to do so.

At the White House, there is an entrance accessible by a ramp for individuals in wheelchairs. Elevator service is available between floors. Prior arrangements should be made so that full attention may be given to provide a comfortable tour. Officers are always on hand to render necessary assistance.

Another accessible structure in the capital is the 555-foot Washington Monument. The 15th Street access is best for wheelchair visitors. An elevator goes to the top. However, the viewing apertures are too high for one seated in a wheelchair.

As a necessary adjunct to touring that requires overnight stops, suitable sleeping arrangements must be secured. Modern hotels, and many of older construction, have some rooms suitable for wheelchair-users. It is best for reservations to be made in advance so that the best available accommodations may be obtained. Any special requirements such as the height of bed and firmness of mattress may be attended to at that time.

Perhaps motels are more "your cup of tea." If so, try to ascertain through the American Automobile Association (AAA), the local chamber of commerce, or the tourist bureau whether any motels in the vicinity meet your requirements. Many motels have units suitable for guests using wheelchairs.

TABLE IV
SOME MOTELS WITH WHEELCHAIR UNITS*

Alabama		
Florence	TraveLodge	402 East Tennessee
Arizona		
Flagstaff	Highway House	2510 E. Santa Fe Avenue
Glendale	Sage Motel	6940 N.W. Grand Avenue
Mesa	TraveLodge	20 S. Country Club Drive
Phoenix	Highway Inn	1735 Grand Avenue
Tucson	Highway House	1601 Miracle Mile Strip
Yuma	Royal Inn	2941 4th Avenue U.S. Hwy. 80 East
California		
Anaheim	TraveLodge	1166 W. Katella Avenue
Barstow	Royal Inn	1350 W. Main Street
El Monte	Royal Inn	12040 E. Garvey Avenue
Needles	Royal Inn	Arch and Q Streets
Palm Springs	Royal Inn	1700 S. Palm Canyon Drive
San Diego	Royal Inn	4875 Harbor Drive
	Royal Inn	9th and Ash Streets
San Francisco	Town House	8th and Market Streets
Santa Barbara	Royal Inn	128 Castillo Street
Santa Cruz	TraveLodge	525 Ocean Street

*This is only a representative list of motels with wheelchair units. There are many others in the United States and Canada. Blueprints for such units are available at no charge by writing: M. C. Montgomery, 1301 N. Park Avenue, Casa Grande, Arizona 85222.

Colorado

Durango	TraveLodge	475 Second Street
Grand Junction	TraveLodge	104 White Avenue
Greeley	TraveLodge	721 13th Street

Florida

Clearwater	TraveLodge	711 Cleveland Avenue
Fort Myers	TraveLodge	2038 W. First Street
Jennings	Holiday Inn	Interstate 75 and State Road 143
Marianna	Holiday Inn	U.S. Hwy. 90, East
Panama City	TraveLodge	900 Harrison Street
Pensacola	TraveLodge	200 E. Palafox
Stuart	Holiday Inn	1209 S. Federal Hwy.

Georgia

Atlanta	TraveLodge	311 Courtland Street, N.E.
Savannah	TraveLodge	512 W. Oglethorpe Avenue

Idaho

Boise	Holiday Inn	Interstate 80 and Vista Avenue

Illinois

Alton	TraveLodge	717 E. Broadway

Indiana

Bloomington	TraveLodge	2615 E. Third Street
Evansville	TraveLodge	701 First Avenue
South Bend	TraveLodge	614 N. Michigan

Iowa

Ames	TraveLodge	229 S. Duff Street
Ft. Dodge	Holiday Inn	116 Kenyon Road
	TraveLodge	300 First Avenue, South
Mason City	TraveLodge	24 Fifth Street, S.W.

Kentucky

Frankfort	TraveLodge	711 E. Main Street
Paducah	TraveLodge	1234 Broadway

Louisiana

Monroe	TraveLodge	401 Grammont

Massachusetts

S. Attleboro	Holiday Inn	Newport Avenue and Interstate 95

Michigan

Dearborn	TraveLodge	23730 Michigan Avenue
Detroit	TraveLodge	1999 E. Jefferson

Minnesota

St. Paul	TraveLodge	149 E. University

Mississippi

Vicksburg	Holiday Inn	Highway 80, East

Missouri

Kansas City	TraveLodge	921 Cherry Street
St. Louis	Parkway House	3570 Lindbergh

Montana

Butte	Holiday Inn	2910 S. Harrison Avenue

Nebraska

South Sioux City	TraveLodge	400 Dakota Avenue

New Jersey

Lyndhurst	Holiday Inn	State Routes 3 and 17

New Mexico

Albuquerque	TraveLodge	3711 Central Avenue, N.E.
	Highway House	3200 Central Avenue, S.E.
	Holiday Inn	12901 Central Avenue, N.E.

New York
Newburgh	Ka-Jax Motel	Box 481, Route 9-W
Niagara Falls	TraveLodge	200 Jefferson Avenue

North Carolina
Henderson	Holiday Inn	U.S. Hwy. 1 and Interstate 85
Raleigh	TraveLodge	300 N. Dawson Street

Ohio
Kent	Holiday Inn	Intersection of Routes 43 and 80
Lima	TraveLodge	418 W. Market Street

Oklahoma
Tulsa	Highway House	5311 W. Skelly Drive

Oregon
Medford	TraveLodge	722 N. Riverside Avenue
Roseburg	TraveLodge	315 W. Harvard

Pennsylvania
Chambersburg	TraveLodge	565 Lincoln Way, East
West Mifflin	Holiday Inn	3 Lebanon Church Road

South Carolina
N. Charleston	Holiday Inn	Calhoun and Savannah Streets

Tennessee
Dyersburg	Holiday Inn	U.S. Hwy. 51, North
Nashville	TraveLodge	800 James Robertson Pkwy.

Texas
Del Rio	Holiday Inn	U.S. Hwy. 90, West
El Paso	TraveLodge	6308 Montana Street

Utah
Provo	TraveLodge	124 S. University
Salt Lake City	TraveLodge	215 West N. Temple Street

Virginia
Danville	Holiday Inn	Riverside Drive at Piney Forest Road

Washington
Bellevue	TraveLodge	11011 N.E. Eight Street

Wyoming
Casper	Holiday Inn	300 West "F" Street
Laramie	TraveLodge	262 N. Third Street

Chapter 4

PLAN WISELY FOR HIGHER LEARNING

THE WHEELCHAIR-USER who desires to advance his education is having many new scholastic doors opened. Before starting college, he should assure himself that hard work will not daunt him. Then, like a general going into the front lines, the disabled student should carefully select his "battlefield."

First, the student should ascertain a college which offers a course of study leading to the goal he has in mind. Then he should examine the facilities at the institution to determine if they are compatible with the requirements caused by his disability. He should try to find more than one that fits the bill.

Factors to be considered in determining the college's accessibility are ramps to school buildings, dormitories, and other buildings; reserved parking areas and beveled curbs; availability of vocational rehabilitation services; suitable toilet facilities; and the experience of the institution in handling wheelchair students.

The next step is to write the registrar to ascertain the school's requirements. It is suggested that the student give a brief statement as to his requirements so that if the institution's facilities are wanting, he will be told at once before expending time and energy.

Many students manage to get along fairly well on their own. For one who cannot, careful investigation is a must. *Before* going to the campus to look it over, he must find out if arrangements can be made for the employment of a student attendant. He must enumerate in detail the services he will need to assist the college in finding the right person for the job.

As a condition precedent, the institution may require such a disabled candidate to sign a waiver of liability form, the purpose being to exonerate the school from responsibility for injuries arising because of the student's physical condition. This is not unreasonable as long as the injury is not caused by negligence on the part of the college.

The form should not provide that the institution be absolved even if negligent. When there is the slightest doubt about signing the form, a lawyer's opinion should be sought.

Some institutions offer extraordinary services to disabled applicants:

1. Preadmission counseling and evaluation are arranged.
2. In addition to normal orientation, facilities and services for the disabled are outlined.
3. Arrangements are made for medical services, physical therapy, and occupational therapy at the rehabilitation center of the college.
4. The *Delta Sigma Omicron* coeducational service fraternity of physically handicapped students, promotes the academic, physical, and social welfare of disabled students. It was incorporated under Illinois law in 1949.
   a. It investigates occupational opportunities.
   b. It has as its motto: "To exercise our abilities to a maximum so as to minimize our disabilities, that we may live most and serve best."

At the University of Illinois, students who are in wheelchairs or who are otherwise disabled may pursue any regular academic study that is physically and mentally feasible. This institution gives preference to residents of Illinois over out-of-state applicants, although the latter are carefully considered.

In addition to the requirements to be generally followed when applying, disabled students must:

1. Have a comprehensive medical report sent to the university's Rehabilitation-Education Center, Oak Street at Stadium Drive, Champaign, Illinois.
2. Must be personally interviewed at the institution.
3. Must take a Psychometric Test and send the results thereof to the campus before the applicant's interview. This test consists of:
   a. School and College Ability Test.
      (1) Given under timed and untimed conditions to give information as to the candidate's ability to handle problems resulting from his disability.
   b. The Strong Vocational Interest Blank.

    c. Edwards Personal Preference Schedule.

    d. Wechsler Adult Intelligence Scale.

       (1) A *full* psychological assessment of the applicant, including a report of any clinical evidence derived from the administration of any other tests such as the Rorschach.

Another educational institution with an interesting concept concerning disabled students is Ferris State College in Michigan. Its policy is to offer opportunity for advanced education to *any* mature person of good character who sincerely desires to advance himself. Consistent with this open-door philosophy, curricula and physical aspects on the campus have been adapted to meet the needs of many disabled students.

The college makes no distinction between the disabled and able-bodied student, except where physical limitations require modification. As a matter of fact, the disabled are encouraged to become active in social as well as academic activities on the theory that a well-rounded education consists of more than just "book learning."

In addition to the academic studies, students are encouraged to improve social skills so as to achieve a maximum of self-reliance and independence. As part of this feature of education, the disabled find that participating in glee club and band work, as well as in student government groups, is extremely helpful in integrating them in campus society.

The physical aspect of the college is conducive to bringing out the best in disabled students when it comes to doing for themselves. The campus is compact, with all buildings close to one another. Ramps and cut-away curbs are strategically located. Special reserved parking zones are in close proximity to all buildings. Dormitories have street-level entrances. Multistory buildings are equipped with elevators in most instances. If such buildings do not have elevators, ground-floor classroom assignments are made for the disabled (Figs. 28 and 29).

With respect to housing, special consideration is given wheelchair-users. They are assigned rooms in easily accessible dormitories, with bathroom facilities adapted to their requirements. Beds have been altered, making it easier to use them from a wheelchair.

During orientation and registration week, wheelchair students are given first chance in scheduling classes so as to work out the best class assignments for their physical needs. Educational and rehabilitation counselors are always available.

Despite the desire of Ferris State College to offer educational opportunities to all, the school authorities are realists. For physiotherapy, psychiatry, orthopedic treatment, and eye services, one requiring such attention would have to travel to Grand Rapids, a distance of 60 miles. Therefore, the college is not suited for those needing such treatment and supervision.

The college has formulated a level of independence required for acceptance that is similar to the criteria of other institutions. Factors included are

1. The ability to navigate independently.
2. A capability of taking care of personal needs without the assistance of anyone.
3. Possession of such a health level as to come within the framework of the medical services available.

Although assistance is usually available, this is not always the case. *Independence* is most desirable.

Chapter 5

DOWN BARRIERS—UP EDUCATION

WITH A SPIRALING population, time is of the essence in the program to make educational facilities accessible to every ambitious student, disabled or able-bodied. In this rapidly expanding world with ever-increasing challenges, institutions of learning and academic curricula must be broadened so as to offer a spectrum of courses unprecedented in scope.

Reports received from numerous campuses reflect an almost phenomenal improvement in their physical aspects. Students, upon their return from summer vacations, are often astounded to see buildings open for business that *were* "only gleams in someone's eye". These structures include dormitories, lecture halls, laboratories, and libraries. An outstanding feature which they enjoy in common is a lack of architectural barriers against the disabled.

Up to the present it seemed that, when it came to blasting these structural stumbling blocks, educational facilities were treated like forgotten stepchildren. That picture has changed completely—and all for the good.

Facing the situation squarely, it was decided by the committees formed to combat these barriers that a most effective attack on the problem was first, securing the full cooperation of the college presidents. This phase was easy. These educators needed no urging when they learned the purpose of the campaign. They were well aware that poorly designed buildings deprived many persons of the opportunity to take advanced education because their disabilities were not of a type that could surmount flights of steps. Wheelchair occupants were most adversely affected.

As serious as was the deprivation experienced by these would-be students, the loss was more tragic for society in the long run. It may never be known how many of those with great potential in the arts and sciences have been shoved into a mediocre sphere of endeavor.

The universities themselves have directly felt the harm caused by the building barriers when skilled members of their faculties have become disabled. These members may have had much to contribute to the cause of education, but what could they contribute when the fine lecture halls or laboratories that they called "home" became inaccessible?

The tide now has turned; by steady erosion of the old and by thoughtful planning of the new, architectural barriers in educational institutions are crumbling and becoming a thing of the past.

It is heartwarming to reflect on some specific examples. At the University of Florida, a 5-million-dollar student union building, some new structures for various installations such as a multimillion-dollar nuclear science building, a complex for the College of Architecture and Fine Arts, and a number of other edifices were erected, all totally free of architectural barriers to the disabled.

The University of South Florida at Tampa, Florida Presbyterian College at St. Petersburg, and New College in Sarasota, Florida, have likewise improved their facilities, adding new lecture halls, laboratories, and other structures that augment campus life socially as well as intellectually. Thanks to the *lack* of architectural barriers, every student, wheelchair-bound or able-bodied, is on a par with every other. The former required no special assistance and thus do not feel embarrassingly conspicuous.

During recent years, the University of Illinois at Urbana and Champaign has made great strides to eradicate architectural barriers from the paths of disabled students. Supplementing the rehabilitation of buildings to accommodate all, this university has a rehabilitation program for the students themselves, with the ultimate goal being that if one attending the institution has the desire to enter a profession such as engineering or a science, he should be permitted to do so ". . . instead of being channeled into watchmaking or left to sit in idleness."

At the University of Illinois, the first requirement of the disabled candidate is that he must be able to navigate alone. The purpose of this rule is to assure the disabled student of being integrated into normal campus life. He is completely independent to come and go wherever and whenever he pleases, without seeking or receiving special treatment.

Realizing that the disabled require certain consideration, they are permitted, in advance of the regular registration period with its hustle and bustle, to plan schedules that fit their requirements. Classes which are most conveniently reached may thus be selected before they are filled by others.

This university believes that each individual enrolled in a program leading to a specific vocation should also be provided with a program to develop socially, emotionally, and physically.

With this in mind, an athletic program has been formulated which includes sports such as baseball, basketball, bowling, archery, and field and track events. The accomplishments of these wheelchair athletes have become internationally famous. In the September of 1960 Paralympics held in Rome, Italy, eight of the university's students participated; they brought home ten world records and more medals than any other people in the entire Olympics. The Paralympics was only a relatively small part of the Olympic Games. Wheelchair competitors came from twenty-three other countries.

One of the most graceful events at the university, and a source of great pleasure, is square dancing in wheelchairs. This not only offers the participants recreation but is an emotional outlet of sorts that gives the disabled a feeling of being the same as the nondisabled.

However, uppermost in every student's mind is successfully completing his studies. The wonderful record speaks for itself. In a recent year, the scholastic average of the disabled students, more than half of whom were in wheelchairs, was above the level of the ablebodied students. In 1961, one of the salutatorians was a co-ed in a wheelchair. Many of such disabled graduates have gone on to earn master's degrees and doctorates. Among the graduates in wheelchairs, there are teachers, a minister, a physician, and a rehabilitation counselor.

The architectural features which contribute so very much to making the college careers of seriously disabled students successful have been almost universally accepted by institutions throughout the country. Many already have taken appropriate steps against structural "disabilities." Others have just started programs to that effect.

The State of New York, in its effort to eliminate such barriers from the state university, has established a performance criterion regarding the designing, planning, and construction of buildings with facilities accessible to the disabled student as well as the able-bodied.

Governor Nelson A. Rockefeller has created a Council on Rehabilitation and an Interdepartmental Health and Hospital Council which recommend how state buildings should be built or modified to facilitate their use by the disabled. The state university comes within the realm of these councils.

The study conducted in developing the standards for the university structure was conducted in collaboration with numerous authorities in physical medicine and rehabilitation, among whom were

1. Dr. Timothy Nugent, Director of the University of Illinois Rehabilitation Center, and a pioneer in the university's acceptance of disabled students.
2. Dr. Alfred Cohn, Hofstra University's Coordinator for the Program of Higher Education for the Disabled.
3. Adrian Levy, the Assistant Commissioner of Education for Rehabilitation in New York State's Department of Education.

The result was a comprehensive pamphlet recommending many features which will make the university facilities completely accessible to all, regardless of the nature of their disabilities. Included in the contents are doorways, steps and ramps, elevators, electric switches, telephones, parking lot suggestions, restroom recommendations, interiors of dormitories and other campus buildings, and several other items to add to the usability of the facilities by the disabled.

One of the most effective projects on the subject of education for the disabled at institutions of higher learning was conducted under a grant from the Vocational Rehabilitation Administration of the U.S. Department of Health, Education, and Welfare. A lengthy report covering rehabilitation, health education, administrative procedures, building and equipment facilities, and many other subjects was edited by William V. Tucker, M.S., research director and instructor of psychology at Briar Cliff College, Sioux City, Iowa. Named as project directors were Dr. Harry J. Waters, Professor of Education and Head of the Counselor at Kansas State Teachers College, Emporia, Kansas, and Dr. Eugene S. Edgington, Associate Professor of Psychology at the University of Alberta, Calgary, Canada.

The Foreword to the booklet containing the report, written by John E. King, President of Kansas State Teachers College, expresses so well the purpose of this and similar projects. ". . . Every individual must be given the opportunity to achieve his intellectual potential, regardless of the physical stature of the man. . . . A sincere belief in the worth and dignity of the individual has prompted many colleges and universities throughout the United States to accept this challenge. . . . These institutions have found that their efforts have been well rewarded as many of their handicapped graduates have become useful teachers, lawyers. . . ."

During the past decade, numerous institutions have adapted their curricula and facilities specifically to make it convenient for the disabled to pursue a course of studies. Typical of the colleges foremost in making such improvements is Kansas State Teachers College.

Strategically placed ramps have been installed to facilitate entering and leaving buildings. All structures with floors above ground level have ample elevators. Special bathroom facilities have been provided. Dormitories have been furnished with the requirements of the disabled in mind. Apartments, off and on campus, have been modified for the benefit of those who desire to do their own housekeeping and cooking.

This college has a natural advantage. Its campus is relatively flat and compact. To make locomotion easier for students in wheelchairs, curbs have been lowered, at intervals, to the street level (Fig. 28).

In order not to make the program too difficult for colleges wishing to accommodate themselves to handling disabled students, the adaptations are kept at a minimum. Too many facilities and services would be extremely costly. Even worse, like an overdose of sugar in a cup of coffee, these would act to the student's detriment by not giving him the opportunity to cope with the problems which he could actually handle without assistance.

Contrary to what once was the popular belief that a very few universities had experience in educating the disabled, almost one thousand institutions throughout the United States have had many handicapped students—in wheelchairs, with hearing and sight impairments, and with other disabling conditions—to graduate, to enter diversified fields of endeavor, and to become great successes.

Table V contains a list of universities and colleges which have made provision to accommodate students in wheelchairs. The institutions tabulated had wheelchair students enrolled at the time of the survey. However, facilities and types of enrolled students change continuously.

TABLE V

Alabama

Birmingham Southern College
Howard College
Jacksonville State College
Troy State College

Arizona

Arizona State College
Arizona State University
Phoenix College

Arkansas

Arkansas State College
Arkansas State Teachers College
Little Rock University
Ouachita Baptist College
University of Arkansas

California

American River Junior College
Bakersfield College
California State Polytechnic College, Pamona
Cerritos Junior College
Citrus Junior College
Coalinga College
College of Marin
College of San Mateo
Compton College
Diablo Valley College
East Los Angeles College
El Camino College
Fresno State College
Los Angeles City College
Los Angeles Pierce College
Los Angeles State College
Los Angeles Valley College
Long Beach State College
Modesto Evening Junior College
Mt. San Antonio College
Napa Junior College
Orange Coast College
Sacramento State College
San Bernadino Valley College
San Diego State College
San Fernando Valley State College
San Francisco State College
San Jose City College
San Jose State College
Santa Ana College
Santa Monica City College
Stanford University
Stockton College
University of California, Berkeley

University of California, Davis
University of California, Los Angeles
University of California, Riverside
University of Santa Clara
Vallejo Junior College
Ventura College
Zweegman School for Medical Secretaries

Colorado
Fort Lewis A. & M. College
Regis College
University of Colorado, Boulder
Western State College

Connecticut
Saint Joseph College
University of Connecticut
University of Hartford
Wesleyan University

District of Columbia
American University

Florida
Florida State University
Manatee Junior College
North Florida Junior College
St. Petersburg Junior College
University of Miami
University of South Florida
University of Tampa

Georgia
Augusta College
Emory University
Georgia Institute of Technology
Georgia State College
Morehouse College
Savannah State College
Women's College of Georgia

Hawaii
University of Hawaii

Idaho
Boise Junior College
North Idaho Junior College
Northwest Nazarene College

Illinois
De Paul University
Eastern Illinois University
Loyola University
Quincy College
Roosevelt University
Southern Illinois University
University of Illinois

Indiana
Ball State Teachers College
Earlham College
Indiana State College
Indiana University
Saint Mary's College

Iowa
Drake University

Iowa State Teachers College
Iowa Wesleyan College
Luther College
State University of Iowa
Upper Iowa University

Kansas

Kansas State Teachers College
Southwestern College
University of Kansas
University of Wichita
Washburn University

Kentucky

Eastern State College
Murray State College
University of Kentucky
University of Louisville

Louisiana

Nicholls State College
Louisiana State University, Baton Rouge
Louisiana State University, New Orleans
McNeese State College
Northeastern Louisiana State College
Tulane University
University of Southwestern Louisiana

Maine

Colby Collebe
St. Joseph's College
University of Maine

Maryland

Loyola College

Massachusetts

American International College
Boston College
Harvard University
Massachusetts Institute of Technology
University of Massachusetts

Michigan

Central Michigan University
Ferris Institute
Flint Community College
Henry Ford Community College
Lansing Community College
University of Detroit
Wayne State University
Western Michigan University

Minnesota

Augsburg College
Bemidji State College
College of St. Thomas
Concordia College, Moorhead
Gustavus Adolphus College
Macalester College
Mankato State College
Minnesota State College at St. Cloud
Moorhead State College
Northwestern College
University of Minnesota, Duluth
University of Minnesota, Minneapolis
Winona State College

Mississippi
  Delta State College
  Jackson State College

Missouri
  Northwest Missouri State College
  St. Louis University
  Southeast Missouri State College
  Southwest Missouri State College
  University of Kansas City
  Washington University

Montana
  Eastern Montana College of Education
  Montana State University
  Rocky Mountain College
  Nebraska State Teachers College, Chadron
  Nebraska State Teachers College, Kearney
  Nebraska State Teachers College, Peru

Nebraska
  Hastings College

New Hampshire
  Dartmouth College
  New England College

New Jersey
  Rutgers University
  Seton Hall University
  Stevens Institute of Technology
  Upsala College

New Mexico
  Eastern New Mexico University
  New Mexico State University

New York
  Barnard College of Columbia University
  Brooklyn College
  C. W. Post College
  D'Youville College
  Hofstra College
  Hunter College
  Marymount College
  Pace College
  St. Bonaventure University
  St. John's University
  State University College at New Paltz
  State University College, Oswego
  Utica College of Syracuse University
  Vassar College

North Carolina
  Atlantic Christian College
  Catawba College
  Elizabeth City State College
  North Carolina College
  North Carolina State College
  North Carolina Wesleyan College
  St. Andrews Presbyterian College
  University of North Carolina
  Western Carolina College

North Dakota
  University of North Dakota

Ohio
>   Baldwin-Wallace College
>   Bowling Green State University
>   John Carroll University
>   Kent State University
>   Miami University
>   University of Akron
>   University of Cincinnati
>   University of Dayton
>   University of Toledo
>   Western Reserve University
>   Xavier University
>   Youngstown University

Oklahoma
>   Bethany Nazarene College
>   East Central State College
>   Northeastern Oklahoma A. & M. College
>   Northeastern State College
>   Oklahoma Christian College
>   Oklahoma City University
>   Oklahoma State Technical
>   Oklahoma State University
>   Southwestern State College
>   University of Oklahoma
>   University of Tulsa

Oregon
>   East Oregon College
>   Pacific University
>   Southern Oregon College
>   University of Oregon

Pennsylvania
>   California State College
>   Dickinson College
>   Kutztown State College
>   Lock Haven State College
>   Susquehanna University
>   Swarthmore College
>   Temple University
>   University of Pittsburgh

Rhode Isand
>   Providence College
>   University of Rhode Isand

South Carolina
>   Medical College of South Carolina
>   Wofford College

South Dakota
>   Black Hills Teachers College
>   University of South Dakota

Tennessee
>   Austin Peay State College
>   East Tennessee State University
>   George Peabody College for Teachers
>   Memphis State University
>   Middle Tennessee State College
>   Tennessee Polytechnic Institute

Texas
Abilene Christian College
A. &. M. College of Texas
Arlington State College
Baylor University
Del Mar College
East Texas State College
Kilgore College
Midwestern University
North Texas State University
Pan American College
Prairie View A. &. M. College
San Angelo College
San Antonio College
Southern Methodist University
South Texas Junior College
Stephen F. Austin State College
Texarkana College
Texas A. & I. College
Texas Christian University
Texas Southern University
Texas Technological College
Texas Women's University
Trinity University
University of Texas

Utah
Brigham Young University
University of Utah

Virginia
Lynchburg College
Richmond Professional Institute
University of Virginia

Washington
Clark College
Columbia Basin College
Eastern Washington State College
Everett Junior College
Grays Harbor College
Pacific Lutheran University
Seattle Pacific College
University of Puget Sound
University of Washington
Whitman College
Whitworth College

West Virginia
Marshall University

Wisconsin
Lawrence College
Marquette University
Milwaukee Institute of Technology
University of Wisconsin, Madison
University of Wisconsin, Milwaukee
Wisconsin State College, Eau Claire
Wisconsin State College, La Crosse
Wisconsin State College, River Falls

Wyoming
Casper College
University of Wyoming

CAMPUS FACILITIES

Modification of existing structures and areas, and the establishment of new ones, should be accomplished with the thought constantly in mind that the wheelchair student will be unassisted.

Suggested Specifications

1. *Wheelchairs.* See Tables II and III for facts about the dimensions of the average wheelchair.
2. *Ramps.* These structures permit the wheelchair student to enter and leave all buildings without assistance. An interesting observation is that most student bodies and faculties, whether individuals are disabled or not, prefer to use ramps rather than steps (Figs. 24, 25, and 27).

   The most usual types are those:
   - a. Sloping upward from street level to building entrance.
   - b. Inclined alongside the building, with a level area at the top to turn and enter the doorway.
   - c. Sloping alongside the structure to a basement window which may be altered to serve as an entrance, with a suitable ramp continuing inside.

   The grade should not exceed 1 foot in 12 feet of length. There should be level platforms, about 5 feet square, at regular intervals if the ramp exceeds 30 feet. This affords the wheelchair pusher a rest area. Similar level platforms should be at the bottom, and at the top if there is a door that swings out. The platform should extend at least 1 foot on each side of the doorway.

   The ramp surface should be hard and smooth, but nonskid.
   - a. Wooden ramps can be given added traction by sprinkling sand on a freshly painted surface.
   - b. Concrete ramps may be roughened by jabbing the cement, while still soft, with the bristles of a broom. Steam pipes under the surface will prevent an accumulation of ice and snow in the winter.

   Handrails should be installed about 32 inches above the ramp's surface, so that they may be reached by one in a wheelchair.
   - a. Wooden rails do not rust, are easy to grasp, and do not become excessively hot or cold according to the weather.

b. Metal rails are sometimes preferred because they are splinter-free and because hands can slide along them easily (Fig. 30).

Ramps should be wide enough for all sizes of wheelchairs, with a curb on both sides to prevent the chair from rolling off the edge. If control of the chair is lost on ascent or descent, it can be slowed down or stopped by turning it against the curb. A suggested distance between curbs is 3 feet.

3. *Walks, pavements, and floors.* Surfaces should be hard and smooth, but not slick.

   a. *Concrete sidewalks.* These may be roughened, as in the case of ramps, by jabbing the cement while wet with broom bristles. Sidewalks should have less grade than ramps or none at all since walks are usually longer and have no protective rails.

   b. *Asphalt paving.* This should be sprinkled with crushed stone while the surface is soft. After it hardens, it will be smooth and will provide for good traction. The disadvantage of asphalt is that in hot weather it softens, and wheelchair wheels will sink into it.

   c. *Floors.* These should be ample in width, with smooth hard surfaces that are not slippery. If wax is applied, it should be the nonskid type.

   d. *Gratings and manholes.* Gratings of parallel bars should be avoided. If essential, they should be at right angles to the direction of travel to reduce the danger of wheelchair wheels from slipping between the bars. Covers of manholes should be flush with road.

   e. *Curbs.* Where walks meet other surfaces at different levels, a ramp will blend the difference for the benefit of wheelchair-users. Curbs should be cut down only at ramp sites. They are safety factors, especially for the blind. The latter become aware of a street crossing when their canes touch the curb edge.

4. *Doors, doorways, and entrances.* Doorway surfaces should be hard, smooth, and nonskid. There should be no threshold.

   a. *Interior.* These doors should be wide enough for the average wheelchair to pass through and should be easily operated. They should swing outward to prevent the possibility of being blocked by someone inside falling against the door.

b. *Exterior.* These doors should be at least 36 inches wide and easily operated, swinging outward. Door closers with variable resistance settings are preferable over those that cannot be adjusted. A maximum closing tension of eight pounds is suggested.

Power operated doors may be triggered electrically, hydraulically, or pneumatically. The most popular devices include a photocell, an electric key or push-button switch, and the mat contact. The latter is most suitable, since the door remains open as long as there is pressure on the mat on either side of the doorway (Fig. 21).

Time-delay controls may be hazardous to slow-movers and are not recommended.

c. *Types of doors.* Sliding doors are often more satisfactory than side-hung doors for wheelchair-users since the latter type are frequently placed in awkward positions.

   (1) *Side-hung.* If a side-hung door is in a corner position, it should swing against an adjacent wall. If the door is in a lateral position at the end of a corridor, the knob should be on the side away from the corner, unless the door is hinged at least 6 inches from the wall.

   Double action swinging doors, although not generally recommended because they may prove hazardous, sometimes are the only satisfactory ones to replace poorly placed side-hung doors in existing structures.

   (2) *Sliding.* Single-leaf straight doors are more easily operated. If the in-wall space is too small for a single-leaf door, the bipartite door sliding on a single track in opposite directions in the wall is suggested.

   The door opening should be wide enough to permit passage of a wheelchair with ease, taking into consideration the possibility of an oblique approach. A minimum of 34 inches is advised.

(3) *Revolving.* These doors are not usable by those in
   wheelchairs.

d. *Door handles.* These should be within easy reach for one
   seated in a wheelchair. A minimum of 42 inches above the
   floor is suggested.

   The lever type is preferred. Knobs that may be readily
   gripped are also recommended. Smooth knobs may be given
   a rougher surface by applying adhesive plaster.

e. *Thresholds.* These should be avoided or kept to a minimum
   height. Anything more than ½ inch high may be insurmountable for a wheelchair-user.

   If necessary to make outside doors draft-proof, a piece of
   plastic tubing that will compress under pressure, placed
   against the side of the riser where it meets the floor, may
   substantially reduce the threshold's obstruction.

5. *Switches and controls.* A height of 42 inches from the floor is suggested. The rocker-type switch is preferred as easiest to operate.
   Where possible, the door handle and light switches should be at
   the same height from the floor.

   Elevator control buttons should be easily reached by one in a
   wheelchair. Control buttons for signals and alarms should likewise
   be installed within convenient reach from a wheelchair.

6. *Telephones.* The conventional telephone booth is inaccessible for
   a wheelchair occupant. The telephone company will render maximum cooperation in installing equipment in a most convenient
   manner. See the Chapter 8, which is devoted to telephones.

   It is advisable that public telephones be attached to the wall
   with the dial and receiver cradle no more than 48 inches from the
   floor (Fig. 31).

   Push-button dialing and a loudness control should be incorporated if feasible (Figs. 32 and 33).

7. *Water fountains.* There should be at least one usable fountain on
   each floor. The controls should be hand operated and should be
   located in front.

   The fountain used by wheelchair occupants should be mounted
   with its basin 36 inches above the floor. Fountains should not be
   recessed.

   There are wall-mounted fountains accessible to those in wheelchairs. Paper cup dispensers should be placed within easy reach next to the fountain.

8. *Parking accommodations.* The spaces provided for disabled individuals should be so-designated and identified with a "Reserved" sign (Figs. 22 and 24).

These parking lots should be in close proximity to building entrances.

A width of 10 feet for each space will provide adequate room for a car, with adequate clearance between it and the adjoining space.

The location of parking space should be planned so that individuals in wheelchairs should not be required to go behind parked vehicles when leaving or entering the area. A driver backing from a parking space may not be able to see a person in a wheelchair immediately behind the car.

If the area permits, parking along the curb parallel to the sidewalk will allow the wheelchair-user to leave or enter the car without going in front or behind the car.

9. *Bus service.* Whenever it is financially feasible, an excellent solution to the problem of transporting students in wheelchairs expeditiously on large campuses is a bus equipped with a hydraulic lift (Fig. 34).

Another method, less elaborate and costly, is a vehicle modified with a ramp at the rear door. If a ramp is used, a platform at bus level can serve to facilitate loading of wheelchair students. In such case, the ramp will take the student to the platform surface where he can await the bus. It is suggested that the loading zone be sheltered.

For safety of riders in the vehicle, provision should be made for securely fastening wheelchairs inside the bus to prevent toppling over or other accidental motion caused by sudden stops or turns by the bus.

The Anthony Company, Streator, Illinois, has a hydraulic lift on the market which attaches to the rear door of a bus.

Hints for Planning the Dormitory

To make any building completely accessible to the disabled requires careful attention to details concerning its innards as well as exterior facilities. The following items must be given prime consideration when planning an educational institution that will accommodate *all*:

1. *Restroom, bathroom.* On floors most convenient for wheelchair students and in a few rooms, there should be specially designed facilities.

   a. *Toilet stalls.* The wall-hung commode is most desirable. Its height may be set easily to suit the average wheelchair-user; it permits close frontal approach and facilitates floor cleaning in the surrounding area (Fig. 15).

   The floor-mounted bowl may have its height varied by setting it on a pedestal. The lower part of its exterior surface should recede as much as possible to permit close approach by a wheelchair before the footrests come in contact with it (Fig. 16).

   A convenient height for the toilet seat is the height of the average wheelchair seat. Approximately 20 inches from the floor is suggested.

   The toilet compartment should be at least 36 inches wide and 66 inches deep, with the "john" centered in the rear. If the compartment has a door, it should be at least 32 inches wide and should swing out. The flushing device should be a conveniently positioned lever or pull knob.

   b. *Showers.* The stall type is preferred. It is suggested that the compartment be not less than 4 feet square. A folding waterproof seat should be hung from one wall at the same height as the average wheelchair seat.

   The floor should slope away from the entrance to the cubicle with a drain in the far corner. This will eliminate the need for any riser at the entry to stop the water from flowing into the bathroom.

   A long-neck, adjustable, shower head with flexible side sprays should be provided. Faucet handles should be provided. Faucet handles should be placed close to the shower seat. A single faucet that mixes the hot and cold water to the desired temperature is recommended. Wrist type handles for water control, with a thermostat to prevent scalding, are suggested.

The floor surface inside the stall should be nonslip. Soap trays and towel rods should be about 42 inches above the floor.

c. *Bathtubs.* A bathroom with a tub should have a nonslip floor. The tub should have a seat in it (Fig. 5). There is the stool-type seat that wedges between the sides, and the bench that extends over the side. Many find it easier to transfer from wheelchair to such a bench rather than transferring over the side of the tub.

For those who have difficulty in entering or leaving a bathtub, the Hoyer and similar lifts are commercially available.

d. *Grab rails.* These should be of a diameter that is easily gripped—about 1½ inches is suggested, with a clearance of 1½ inches from the wall.

There should be a horizontal rail on each side of the toilet stall, as well as around the inside walls of the shower and on three sides of the bathtub. Rails that attach to the side of the tub are on the market. A suggested height above the floor for grab rails is 33 inches.

The horizontal rail is helpful in pushing; the vertical helps in pulling; the diagonal one serves both purposes. The latter type is more useful to the ambulant person than to the wheelchair-user.

e. *Wash basins.* These should be hung on the wall by brackets or set in a counter top, with no pedestals or supporting legs to interfere with the knees of one in a wheelchair.

The sink apron should be narrow, with a clearance of about 30 inches from the floor. Faucets should be easily manipulated, and not the self-closing type.

Hot water pipes under the sink should be insulated to prevent the possibility of burns in case of contact with the pipes.

f. *Mirrors.* The bottom of the mirror should be no more than 36 inches above the floor. The mirror should be close to the sink if feasible, with a double electric outlet close by. Students may wish to use electric razors, toothbrushes, and other electrical appliances.

Outlets should be approximately 46 inches above the floor.

g. *Urinals.* Wheelchair-users generally prefer the privacy of commodes, thus obviating the need of urinals.

If these are installed, they should be the wall-hung type, with the front rim not more than 18 inches above the floor.

Since urinals are used by those who are able to stand, vertical grip rails should be attached to the wall on each side of this facility to assist in making its use easier.

2. *Rooms.* There should be ample floor space for easy wheelchair maneuvering. The space between bed and dresser or desk should be at least 50 inches.

Furniture designed for use by the disabled student, despite its having unique features, should be compatible with such items used by the able-bodied.

a. *Beds.* These should be the same height as the average wheelchair seat, about 20 to 22 inches above the floor.

The mattress should be firm, about 6 inches thick, made of foam rubber, or upholstered inner-spring construction with a strong edging. There should be air vents permitting air to circulate in the mattress. An advantage of core foam rubber is that it allows the circulation of air around the pressure points of the body.

There should be storage space beneath the bed that can easily be reached by the occupant of the bed. This can provide convenient storage room for such items as bedpan or urinal.

b. *Desks.* A large, uncluttered surface with kneehole space of about 28 inches along with ample drawer space is desirable.

Formica® covering of the desk will minimize staining and marring.

The desk surface should be as wide as available

space will permit and should be at least 30 inches above the floor. There should be no aprons to impede the knees of a wheelchair student from comfortably fitting under the desk. This also applies to tables.

c. *Lamps.* Bed and desk lamps may be suspended from the wall behind the furniture in such a position, and adjustable, so that maximum illumination will be furnished without shadows. Easily reached switches should be installed.

d. *Telephones.* These should be conveniently placed with an extra long wire leading from wall to instrument so that they may be moved to any surface in the room convenient to the wheelchair student.

The telephone company will cooperate to the maximum in an endeavor to adapt their equipment to the needs of disabled persons. (See Chapter 8).

Adapting Other Facilities

1. *Dining halls.* Dining tables, rectangular in shape, with a surface 30 inches above the floor are desirable. Formica tops are suggested since they are more resistant to marring than is plain wood. There should be no aprons or any other impediments to prevent the knees of wheelchair students from fitting comfortably beneath.

Floors should be nonslip.

Self-service water faucets should be usable by wheelchair students.

The slide for serving trays should be at least 34 inches wide and 32 inches from the floor.

2. *Lecture halls.* These facilities should be easily accessible and in close proximity to parking areas.

a. Space for wheelchairs should be provided in front of the fixed seats but not obstructing the vision of others at the lectures.

3. *Laboratories.* These facilities should be easily accessible to wheelchair students. Equipment and material should be readily usable by one seated in a wheelchair.

Work surfaces should be at least 32 inches above the floor, with knee space of approximately 30 inches. There should be no aprons attached to the work table that may impede the knees from fitting beneath.

A fire extinguisher should be conveniently hung on a wall 42 inches from the floor. If a fire alarm box is installed, it should be at a similar height, with a simple, easily grasped pull-type handle.

4. *Gymnasium*. Most handicapped students are physically unable to partake of regular physical education subjects. However, they can often participate in swimming, archery, and other sports. Therefore these facilities should be accessible to them, and they should have access to the entire athletic area in case they desire to be spectators in events.

Locker rooms should be designed with the disabled student in mind. Toilet and shower facilities should conform to standards that fit their needs.

5. *Theaters and auditoriums*. The disabled student should be permitted to participate in all campus activities, in and outside the classroom. Special seating sections should be reserved for those in wheelchairs.

Access to the stage and dressing rooms should be provided wheelchair students who actively participate in productions.

6. *Administrative offices*. Consideration should be given to the requirements of disabled faculty and staff members when planning these facilities and when furnishing them.

Chapter 6

A BREAK FOR DISABLED SMALL-FRY

IT IS AN ACKNOWLEDGED FACT that a regular neighborhood school is best for all children. This gives them an opportunity to mix with playmates of diversified backgrounds and at the same time is within only a short distance from home if their parents are needed. This is especially necessary for disabled children.

Unfortunately, lack of adequate funds and the nearsightedness of planners result in schools that are inadequate in size so that the ever-mounting student population is causing bulging at the seams. There is scarcely enough room for the able-bodied, let alone the disabled pupil.

Except for an insignificant number of schools that hardly scratch the surface of the number of disabled children wanting education, most others of this category must go into a state of isolation and receive instruction in a class known as the "home-bound." This gives the child an unhealthy feeling of being different.

The time is now at hand for communities to build schools with facilities that can be used by every student, whether able-bodied or not. To accomplish this is not a herculean task.

Civic and business leaders should combine their know-how with officials on all levels of government, together with medical, rehabilitation, and education services, to determine what physical characteristics are essential to make a school accessible to all.

Among the necessary features are
1. No stairs at the entrance, which should be either street level or entered by a ramp.
2. Adequate elevators if the school is higher than the street floor.
3. Wide doorways and corridors.
4. Easily usable toilet facilities.
5. Drinking fountains suitable for wheelchair pupils.
6. Available nursing or medical services.
7. Buses with hydraulic lifts for children in wheelchairs (Fig. 34).

Except for their physical defects, the disabled children are, in most instances, just as alert and eager to learn as their able-bodied brethren. They enjoy reading, studying science, singing, meetings friends, and partaking of life in the normal way that appeals to children in general.

Leading in this program of bringing these countless numbers of children out of seclusion into the mainstream of life is the Human Resources School at Albertson, Long Island, New York.* The students are those with serious physical disabilities who are at the high-school level but no longer can be accommodated in local public schools. The latter, at their best, could only furnish these pupils with a few hours of instruction a week at home.†

The children, many in wheelchairs, are conveyed by specially equipped buses to this modern, one-story structure, whose interior has every modification required by the student body. Wide doors operate automatically by the so-called magic eye. Desks, tables, and shelves are adjustable so that pupils who are in a prone position may be served. There are mirrors which permit the instructor to be seen from diverse angles, and there is a micro-projector for those unable to use the standard microscope. Special laboratory equipment has been designed for use by disabled students who previously had been barred from using such items because of potential danger from gas jets and electrical outlets of the usual type.

For those children who cannot hold writing material, there are electric typewriters which can be easily operated by merely poking

---

*See *A Unique School for the Physically Handicapped* by Frank D. Gentile and J. R. Block.

†New York City Board of Education is forging ahead so as to provide new facilities and adapt existing ones to accommodate orthopedically handicapped children.

1. Special centers have been established with therapy rooms, special speech rooms, and conference rooms.
2. There are buses equipped with hydraulic lifts that permit the loading of children seated in wheelchairs (Fig. 34).
3. All new schools, when feasible, are provided with ramps, anticipating the possibility that these structures may be used in the future for classes for the handicapped. As far as possible, many areas such as lunchrooms, shops, and auditoriums are being situated on the same level so that the disabled child may be readily integrated into the general school pattern.
4. Schools will be built with, or altered to have, special toilets for wheelchair students, wide doors, ample grab rails, convenient entrances.

the keys. Supplementing the academic program, there is an excellent physical therapy course of instruction which includes fencing and bowling.

The school has as one of its aims to help its students adjust to life so that they can enjoy it to the hilt, within their physical limitations. The children bask in the sunshine of being accepted as people. Extremely heartwarming is the sense of independence and self-sufficiency acquired by the students. Their resistance sometimes borders on fierceness when they shout, "Don't help me. I can do it myself!"

The Human Resources School has been designated a pilot project by the New York State legislature, with the state paying $1800 per year for each pupil. The total cost for each student is about $2500 annually, the difference being made up by private contributions.

In addition to the benefits derived from the school, the seriously disabled child, who once was completely home-bound, now has an opportunity to enjoy the everyday experiences of the physically normal. One such pleasure is attending the day camp provided by Easter Seal at Human Resources, Albertson, New York. This facility is financed by the Association for Crippled Children and Adults of New York State in conjunction with the Easter Seal Society.

Priority for camp admission is given to severely disabled children, excluding the mentally retarded and emotionally disturbed. For parents who can afford it, there is a weekly fee of five dollars. The staff includes a director and his assistant (both licensed in special education), medical personnel, a physical therapist, and counselors who teach the campers various subjects of interest such as arts and crafts, wheelchair dancing, painting, and sculpturing.

There are spacious lawns for outdoor activities, while the indoor facilities boast a large auditorium, industrial workshops, cafeterias, a bowling alley with automatic pin setters, and a swimming pool (60 × 70 feet) made of nonskid marble with ramps and steel bars for wheelchair-users.

For field trips there is a bus with wide aisles and a hydraulic lift for wheelchairs (Fig. 34). Structural features are level entrances, wide doors and halls, convenient drinking fountains, and accessible well-equipped restrooms.

The disabled child has an opportunity to develop his individual capacities to the maximum and to attain a high degree of self-confidence and independence within the limits of his physical condition.

Increased competence in using wheelchairs and in self-care seems to increase social development. This is one of the camp's beneficial results. Diminishing the tending toward social withdrawal is another accomplishment: instead of superficial contacts, strong friendships are formed.

Adding the knowledge and benefits derived from Human Resources Camp to the information taught at the school, the child with formidable physical deficiencies may be armed to meet his problems head-on. His world will no longer be the four walls of a shut-in. With his intellectual, social, and cultural horizons broadened, he will become a well-rounded, independent individual.

A fifteen-year-old boy told the story in a few poignant words: "Just think, on my last day at camp, I used the toilet *myself!*"

Chapter 7

HOSPITALS, CURE THYSELVES!

MANY EXISTING HOSPITALS were built in a traditional design that had, as one of its requirements, entrance steps. It is essential for a wheelchair user, or any other person unable to negotiate stairs, to seek an easier way into the sanctuary for health. After expending much energy and sometimes precious time, the only ground-level or ramped entrance may be a distant emergency door.

How often arrivals have commented after reaching the admissions office, "Whew, I didn't think I'd make it." Sometimes they don't!

The principal culprit causing poorly planned hospitals is the same one that plagues the building industry in general—thoughtlessness.

In today's age of awareness of the problems of disabled persons, it seems almost unbelievable that only a few years ago, hospitals were being erected with flights of steps at the entrance, ramps that were dangerously precipitous, narrow doors, inaccessible restrooms, and inadequate parking spaces, just to mention a few inadequacies.

These older hospitals, in many instances, have facilities that are inconvenient for many patients to use; to some patients, use of the facilities is impossible. What good is a bathroom with a door too narrow for a wheelchair to enter? Or, what if the doorway is wide enough but the room is still not suitable because the toilet stall is too small to accommodate a wheelchair?

As a result of any such structural deficiency, added burdens are imposed on hospital staffs which, in most instances, are ordinarily taxed beyond "the call of duty." An employee is required to assist the wheelchair patient into the bathroom and then onto the com-code. If this is not possible, the less satisfying and more time-consuming procedure of using the bedpan must be followed.

Poor door arrangements have caused numerous accidents as, for example, when someone opens a door that strikes against the bathroom door, inevitably banging the patient exiting from the bathroom.

With the progress in recent years of medicine, surgery, and physical rehabilitation, more and better hospital facilities are essential. Architects and hospital planners have had their problems of design amplified, for the requirements of the modern hospital are many and complicated. The services demanded are becoming more specialized and complex. Efficiency and effectiveness must be maintained at the highest level. Existing installations must be modified so that all patients, no matter how seriously disabled they are, may have access to every necessary area.

Although special units and facilities have received primary attention with other features of the hospital "playing second fiddle," a change is occurring because of the increase in extended, long-term convalescent patients requiring rehabilitation treatment. Facilities for those patients are becoming necessary.

The fact that a building is designated as a hospital, with diversified medical activities scheduled to occur there, does not of itself eliminate architectural barriers. Because of the benevolent purpose of the structures, great care and deliberation should be paid to the design.

Doorways should be wide enough for wheelchairs; corridors should be broad; bathrooms should be ample in size, with fixtures easily used; grab bars should be installed generously in positions around toilets, bathing facilities, urinals, and other places where the disabled need added security.

As in the recommended construction for industrial and public buildings, the satisfactory planning of hospitals will be facilitated by turning to the guidelines* established by the American Standards Association. Some of the specifications vital in making hospital facilities more accessible are deserving of being repeated. They are

1. *Ramps.* These should not be steeper than 8 degress with non-slip surfaces, protective side rails, and level spaces at top and bottom.
2. *Entrances.* At least one main entrance should be easily accessible to a wheelchair-user.
3. *Elevators.* Cars hould be large enough to accommodate a

---

*Guidelines appear in the pamphlet, *American Standards and Specifications for Making Buildings Accessible to, and Usable by, the Physically Handicapped.*

wheelchair and an attendant. Controls should be within reach of one seated in a wheelchair.

4. *Doors.* Ample width should permit a wheelchair to pass through with ease. Operation should require a minimum of effort. When possible doors should open and close automatically. Revolving doors are taboo. Thresholds should be reduced to a minimum.

5. *Steps.* These mortal foes of most disabled persons, especially the wheelchair-user, should be obviated as much as possible. This may be accomplished by ramps or by grading the building site so that at least one entrance will be ground level.

6. *Walks.* With at least a 4-foot width, these should have a smooth, nonslip surface and gradient of less than 4 degrees.

7. *Parking lots.* These should be close to each building used by the disabled, with spaces from 10 to 12 feet wide. They should be located so that persons in wheelchairs are not required to wheel behind parked cars.

8. *Restrooms.* Ample space to comfortably accommodate a wheelchair should be provided. At least one toilet stall should be large enough for a wheelchair, with grab rails on each side of the commode.

9. *Drinking fountains.* These should be usable by one in a wheelchair. The wall-hung and recessed types are not recommended unless carefully adapted for use by one in a wheelchair.

10. *Public telephones.* Dial and receiver should be easily reached from a wheelchair. (See Chapter 8).

By eliminating architectural barriers from hospitals, both patients and staff will benefit because of increased ease and safety in using the facilities.

The same accommodations should apply to nursing homes and homes for the aged. Concerning the latter, the New York City Bureau of Building Construction has given special recognition to the needs and mobility of wheelchair-users in designing institutions for the chronically ill and aged.

Gradients of walks have been reduced to the minimum as required for drainage. Doorways have been made wider than those set by the American Standards Committee. Steps and thresholds have been completely eliminated. Spacious paved terrace areas have been provided for the free movement of patients. Where space permits, shelters have been provided at intervals throughout the grounds to protect residents from the elements. For instance, at the Neponsit Home for the Aged in Queens, pergolas were installed to offer cover from direct impact of the sun while allowing partial infiltration of the sun's rays.

Chapter 8

YOUR TELEPHONE
— A LEGACY OF RESPONSIBILITY —

At Goldwater Memorial Hospital on Welfare Island in New York City, a patient answered the telephone. You might ask, "So what?"

Well, that individual was paralyzed from the neck down! Thanks to a recent telephone company invention, a headset and a chin-level micro-switch, a patient may answer the phone merely by nudging the instrument with his chin.

This is only one of innumerable examples of how the Bell System strives continuously to improve communication by the disabled.

Historically, the company's sense of responsibility goes back to the days of Alexander Graham Bell (1847-1922). Bell was born in Edinburgh, Scotland, residing during most of his boyhood on an aptly named thoroughfare, Hope Street. He was exposed to the activities of his father, Alexander Melville Bell (1819-1905), who developed a method to teach the deaf to speak. The system, known as *visible speech,* incorporated a code of symbols made up of curves and straight lines that indicated the action of the throat, tongue, and lips when pronouncing various sounds.

Although visible speech had originally been intended to serve as a key for the proper pronunciation of words in all languages, it became apparent that the method could be employed to guide the deaf in learning speech. Young Bell became an expert in the use of the system for the latter purpose.

Adding impetus in Bell's desire to aid the deaf was the loss of hearing of his mother. Her affliction intensified his interest in alleviating the condition of the deaf. His inventive streak from that time on became much more evident.

In 1869 Aleck moved to London, England, where he worked with his father in giving corrective speech lessons. The following year, the Bell family moved to Canada. In 1872, young Bell settled permanently in Boston, Massachusetts, where he opened a speech school serving not only to give direct instruction to the deaf but also acting as a school for teachers of the deaf.

His classes became famous for achieving phenomenal results. One student who benefited dramatically was Mabel Hubbard, daughter of a prominent Boston attorney. Subsequently, Mabel became Bell's wife. Another student who made great progress under Bell's tutelage was the young son of a prosperous leather merchant, Thomas Sanders. The five-year-old boy, born deaf, began talking!

In 1873, Bell was working on a "multiple harmonic telegraph" that would permit sending more than one Morse message over a single telegraph wire. Out of gratitude to Bell, Thomas Sanders offered to finance the experiments. Mabel's father, Gardiner Greene Hubbard, also desired to "chip in." A business association was formed.

In 1875 the thought of reproducing and transmitting sound via electrical apparatus came to Bell. Working tirelessly with his good friend Thomas A. Watson eventually led to that eventful March 10, 1876, when over the wire was clearly heard, "Watson, come here. I want you." The rest is history.

The present-day attitude of the Bell System, of bettering the lot of the handicapped, is strikingly evidenced over and over again. With the spirit of public service uppermost in their thoughts, the system's inventive employees, with productive ingenuity, have created and installed equipment to meet many special needs.

For most service requirements there is a good deal of diversified standard equipment easily adapted to suit disabled users. However, the company is not satisfied to rest on its laurels with the *status quo.* A centralized "pool of knowledge" has been established to keep improving the services by continuous studies of the public's needs, with an eagle eye on research directed at improving communications.

The disabilities dealt with are multitudinous. Motion infirmities involving the wheelchair-user with no complications in his physical condition other than the inability to ambulate raise few or no problems. In such cases, standard equipment is usually adequate. The only requirement is that when the phone is wall hung or in a booth, the dial and instrument be within easy reach from a wheelchair (Fig 31).

For the individual who finds holding the handset too arduous, there is a headset that may be plugged into a jack installed in the base of the phone. This permits hand-free telephoning (Fig. 35).

The Speakerphone is another instrument which allows phoning without use of the hands. The device is a small, sensitive desk-top microphone into which one may speak using normal conversational tones. The other party's voice is heard over a separate desk-top speaker (Fig. 36).

The home-bound youngster is able to "go to school" by means of a two-way speaker that incorporates in a single instrument the accomplishments of the Speakerphone and receiver. One such device is placed near the student at home and another within range of the teacher's voice (Figs. 37 and 38).

For those who find dialing difficult, the Touch-Tone phone with a panel of ten push buttons numbered from 1 to 0 may be more convenient than the rotary dial. The buttons may be operated by poking them with arthritic fingers, a toe, a prosthetic hand, a mouth stick, or even the tongue (Figs. 32 and 39). Touch-Tone calling is available in many parts of the United States and gradually the service is spreading to other areas.

From time to time, requests are received from persons with visual impairment to have the phone modified to provide features to relieve them of the necessity of relying on sight to dial a number. Once again the company introduced a fascinating solution to the frustrating problem. It was the Card Dialer telephone with Touch-Tone dialing.

Plastic cards with pre-punched numbers for frequently called phone numbers are prepared according to instructions. For the sightless, brailled symbols representing the desired numbers are pasted at the tops of the cards. To complete such a call, the appropriate card is inserted in a slot provided in the Card Dialer, and, merely by pressing a start bar, the dialing mechanism is activated.

Before making any equipment changes, the company endeavors to teach the subscribers a touch system on the *standard* dial. This is actually the preferable procedure. With this ability, the subscriber is not limited to any special instrument. He may use a public phone or one at a place he may be visiting. If sight or light should decline unexpectedly, he could dial for help. Knowledge of this dialing system would be advantageous to persons with normal eyesight if for some unforeseen reason the lights went out.

Of the various touch methods, three suggested ones are

1. The index, middle, and fourth fingers of the dialing hand are placed in the "five," "three," and "one" holes respectively. To locate "two" and "four," it is only necessary to move a finger one position. The same three fingers can be maneuvered to learn the location of the remaining holes, "six," "eight," and "zero," with "seven" and "nine" found by moving a finger one position.

2. When dialing with the right hand, place hand at top of the dial with index finger at "four," the middle finger at "three," the fourth finger at "two," and the pinky at "one." By shifting the index finger one space, "five" may be found. Moving the dialing hand to the bottom of the dial with the index finger at "seven" and the other fingers at "eight," "nine," and "zero," respectively, "six" can be located merely by shifting the index finger one space.

3. Place the index finger of the dialing hand against the finger stop. Slide the finger counterclockwise along the dial's surface, counting the holes and stopping at the desired digit. After that number, follow the same procedure for the remaining digits.

For those with *impaired speech,* there are handsets with volume control units built-in that permit amplification of weak voices (Fig. 33). If the disability involves disorders of the larynx, or even if this vital speech organ has been removed, there is an electronic larynx that "gives voice" to the laryngectomee who is not able to master esophageal speech (Fig. 40).

Many persons with a wide variety of *hearing impairments* can use the standard telephone with a volume control handset. There is also available a bone-conduction receiver with an amplifier. Some hearing aids have a volume control feature for telephone pickup.

The *totally deaf* are confronted by a difficult problem when it comes to telephone communication. They are obliged to rely upon one of the other senses. Touch and sight make the best substitutes for hearing.

The easiest way to send a visual message is with a *teletypewriter.*

This instrument has a keyboard much like that of a regular typewriter, with a continuous roll of paper attached. Each party has one of these instruments at hand. The message is typed out in front of the deaf person on his roll of paper, and he may reply by typing an answer on his own keyboard. Thus, communication is instantaneous with each party receiving a permanent printed record of every word of the conversation.

Telewriting equipment also permits sending a handwritten message. Using a stylus, the message may be written on the roll of paper. At the receiving end, a stylus duplicates every motion of the sender on the roll of paper attached to the receiver.

Use of teletyping equipment has a serious limitation: the deaf person may communicate only with persons having similar apparatus. However, experiments are being conducted with devices which will enable the totally deaf to receive phone messages from any telephone, wherever located. The parties to the conversation must establish a code, whether by whistling or humming dots and dashes in a fashion similar to the Morse code. These sounds made into the telephone are converted into flashes of light or movements of a vibrating button, that can be felt with the fingertips, by a special instrument in front of the person.

Two examples of how the Bell System has devised methods to enable deaf customers to communicate by means other than standard equipment are

1. A husband and wife, both deaf, using the Sensicall sets from different areas, may converse with each other although many miles apart (Morse code used).

2. Equipment furnished may permit a deaf user to see visual representations of code sounds on an oscilloscope screen (Courtesy Pacific Telephone and Telegraph Company).

Another way that a deaf person may receive calls on any phone, without use of a code, is by utilizing the services of a person with normal hearing who is provided with a small single earphone called a Watchcase Receiver. He listens to the distant party's words and repeats them soundlessly. The deaf person reads his lips and replies to the distant party over the regular handset in the normal manner. When Picturephone service is generally available, the deaf person will be able to read the caller's lips by watching the picture on the screen, thus eliminating the middleman.

To alert the person with defective hearing that the phone is ringing, the telephone company can provide bells, gongs, buzzers, and horns of various intensities and frequencies. Another attention-getting device in an electrically controlled switch that turns on lights or electric fans when the phone rings and turns them off when the ringing stops (Fig. 41).

Although it is preferable to use regular equipment whenever feasible, Bell System engineers are constantly devising special items for the handicapped. Each Bell System has a group of experts, known as Coordinators of Telephone Services for the Handicapped, who can be called upon for advice if novel or complicated situations arise. They have access to all information that clears the company's headquarters coordinator. To facilitate their activities, this group may call upon the resources of all Bell System Telephone laboratories and medical consultants.

BIBLIOGRAPHY

BOOKLETS AND PAMPHLETS

KAMENETZ, H.L.: *The Wheelchair Book.* Springfield, Thomas, to be published (1968).

RUSK, HOWARD A., AND LOWMAN, EDWARD W.: *Self-help Devices.* New York, Institute of Rehabilitation Medicine.

SCHNUR, SANDRA: *New York with Ease.* New York, Easter Seal Society.

TUCKER, WILLIAM V.: *Higher Education and Handicapped Students.* Emporia, Kansas State Teachers College.

WHEELER, VIRGINIA HART: *Planning Kitchens for Handicapped Homemakers.* New York, Institute of Rehabilitation Medicine.

Making Facilities Accessible to the Handicapped. Albany, New York State University.

The Functional Home for Easier Living. New York, Institute of Rehabilitation Medicine.

Guide to the National Parks and Monuments for Handicapped Tourists. Washingon, published by the President's Committee on Employment of Handicapped in cooperation with the Veterans Employment Service of the U.S. Department of Labor Manpower Administration.

OTHER

Articles regarding elimination of architectural barriers appeared in the following publications:

Bell Telephone Magazine: Summer, 1965. 195 Broadway, New York City.

Journal of American Insurance: September 1964. 20 North Wacker Drive, Chicago, Ilinois.

Modern Home Lifts, a booklet: Inclinator Company of America, 2200 Paxton Street, Harrisburg, Pennsylvania.

Paraplegia News: September 1966. 935 Coastline Drive, Seal Beach, California.

Rehabilitation Literature: January 1962. 2023 West Ogden Avenue, Chicago, Illinois.

Rehabilitation Record: November-December 1961, September-October 1964. Superintendent of Documents, U.S. Government Printing Office, Washington, D.C.

[129]

The International Altrusan: January 1963. 332 S. Michigan Avenue, Chicago, Illinois.

Toomey-j Gazette: Box 149, Chagrin Falls, Ohio.

Additional information may be found in:

American Standards and Specifications for Making Buildings Accessible to, and Usable by, the Physically Handicapped, a pamphlet.

Catholic Standard: March 31, 1966.

Congressional Record: February 5, 1962. Remarks of Hon. Paul H. Douglas.

Congressional Record: February 6, 1962. Remarks of Hon. John E. Fogarty.

Development of the Wheelchair Lift, a brochure published by the Otis Elevator Company.

Hospitals: February 1, 1966. Published by the American Hospital Association.

New Building Research: Fall, 1960. Published by the Building Research Institute.

Producers' Council's Technical Bulletin 109: September 1964.

Retirement Life: November 1966.

Safety Standards: July-August 1959. President's Committee on Employment of the Handicapped.

The Louisiana Architect: May 1965.

The New York Times: Oct. 30, 1966. Column of Howard A. Rusk, M.D.

The New York Times: December 11, 1966. Column of Howard A. Rusk, M.D.

INDEX

A

Accountant, 9

Acknowledgments
  cooperating agencies, xiii
  individuals, xi-xiii

Air-conditioner, 10, 71

American Automobile Association
    (AAA), 86

American Standards Association
    (Committee), 78
  specifications of, 78-80

Apartments
  adaptation for physical requirements
    bathroom, 4-6, 12, 14, 16, 18
    bedroom, 6, 13, 20
    kitchen, 11, 21, 27
    (*Also see* specific room as listed
      in Index)
  types of apartment buildings
    condominium, 8-9
    cooperative, 8
    garden apartments, 8
    municipal housing, 11-12
    straight rental, 9-10
      lease, 9-10
    (For adaptation to meet physical
      needs, *see* specific room as listed
      in Index)

Architects
  American Institute of, 83
    Kansas City chapter, 83-84
  selection of, 55, 56

Architectural (structural) barriers
  elimination of in
    apartment houses, 3-12, 14, 15, 16
    educational institutions, 89-117
    hospitals, 118-121
    private homes, 12-13, 23, 24
    public buildings, 74-88
    (*Also see* "American Standards
      Association")

Attorney, 8, 9, 54

B

Bathrooms, restrooms, 4-6
  fixtures
    bathtub, 5-6
    commode (toilet, john), 5, 63
    electric outlets, 63
    medicine cabinet, 64
    mirror, 64
    seats, 64
    shower, 5-6, 64
    urinal, 111
    (*Also see* specific fixture heading
      in Index)

Bathtub, 5-6

Bedrooms, 6, 13, 20
  closet, 6, 20
  furnishing, 6

Brokers (realtors), 53, 55

Builders, 55, 56

Building sites, 55

Buses for the disabled, 108
  hydraulic lift, 108

C

Campus facilities for wheelchair
    students, (*Also see*
    "Educational Institutions")
  administrative offices, 113
  classroom buildings, 112, 113
  dormitories, 108-112
  recreational, 113
  transportation, 108
  (*Also see* list of Educational
    Institutions in Index)

Checklist for disabled, 4

Condominium apartments, 8-9
  (*Also see* "Architectural
    (structural) barriers")

Cooperative apartments, 8
  (*Also see* "Architectural
    (structural) barriers")

Curbs
  beveled, 40, 105

[131]